INDEPENDENT LEARNING PROJECT FOR ADVANCED CHEMISTRY

ILPAC
second edition

2

STARTER

CHEMICAL ENERGETICS

REVISED BY ANN LAINCHBURY JOHN STEPHENS ALEC THOMPSON

JOHN MURRAY

■ ACKNOWLEDGEMENTS

We are grateful to CLEAPSS/ASE Laboratory Standards Committee for ensuring that the text meets with current safety recommendations.

Thanks are due to the following examination boards for permission to reproduce questions from past A-level papers: Associated Examining Board: Part A test 3, p. 32 (1993); 5, p. 33 (1990); End-of-unit test 11, p. 69 (1992). Joint Matriculation Board: End-of-unit test 6, p .67 (1991). Oxford and Cambridge Schools Examination Board: End-of-unit test 14, p. 69 (1991). University of Cambridge Local Examinations Syndicate: Part A test 8, p. 34 (1991). University of London Examination and Assessments Council: Exercise 16, p. 28 (L 1979); Exercise 20, p. 30 (L 1981); Exercise 31, p. 45 (N 1978); Exercise 39, p. 55 (L 1980); Part A test 1, p. 32 (L 1992); 2, p. 32 (L 1993); 4, p. 33 (L 1988); End-of-unit test 1, p. 66 (L 1992); 2, p. 66 (L 1992); 3, p. 67 (L 1992); 4, p. 67 (L 1987); 5, p. 67 (L 1989); 7, p. 68 (L 1992); 8, p. 68 (L 1987); 9, p. 68 (L 1990); 10, p. 68 (L 1994); 12, p. 69 (L 1990); 13, p. 69 (L 1977); 14, p. 69 (L 1980); Teacher-marked Exercise, p. 58 (L 1990). Welsh Joint Education Committee: Exercise 30, p. 45 (1977); Exercise 34, p. 50 (1976); Exercise 35, p. 51 (1978); End-of-unit test 15, p. 70 (1990). (The examination boards accept no responsibility whatsoever for the accuracy or method of working in the answers given.)

Photographs by the Last Resort Picture Library. The assistance provided by the staff and students of Roding Valley High School, Loughton, Essex and Tuxford School, Tuxford, Newark, Nottinghamshire for the photographs of the experiments is gratefully acknowledged.

Original material produced by the Independent Learning Project for Advanced Chemistry sponsored by the Inner London Education Authority

First edition published 1983
by John Murray (Publishers) Ltd
50 Albemarle Street
London W1X 4BD

Second edition 1995

British Library Cataloguing in Publication Data
A catalogue record for this book is available from the British Library

ISBN 0-7195-5332-6

Design and layouts by John Townson/Creation
Illustrations by Barking Dog Art

Produced by Gray Publishing
Typeset in 10/12 pt Times and Helvetica

Printed in Great Britain by St Edmundsbury Press Ltd, Bury St Edmunds

CONTENTS

INTRODUCTION TO ILPAC

These notes are intended primarily for students starting an A-level chemistry course which makes extensive use of the ILPAC materials. However, we hope you will find them helpful even if you are using perhaps only one ILPAC volume, and at any time.

You are about to spend up to two years studying A-level chemistry – so please spend a few minutes reading these notes before you begin. This is important and could save you time and effort later.

Firstly, we shall consider ways of studying effectively; secondly, we shall see how ILPAC can help.

■ How should I study?

You may never have asked yourself this question. Your teacher may have guided you so carefully that you have simply had to follow instructions – to copy notes from the blackboard, perhaps, and then to learn them and copy them out again for a test! This can be quite a good way of learning facts, but it doesn't really help you to solve problems. It protects you from thinking and taking decisions – the teacher has done that for you.

As you move towards more advanced studies, however, you must take more responsibility for your own learning – the ability to find things out for yourself is really one of the most valuable skills you can develop and, despite the electronic revolution, your most useful aids are still books.

■ How to use a textbook

Books differ in style and content and you are unlikely to find all you need for A-level chemistry in a single volume. Don't be put off if you still don't understand the topic you looked up after reading about it in one book – try another one. If you are still in difficulties, then you should go to your teacher, but you'll be surprised how quickly you realise the strengths and weaknesses of the books available to you.

'How should I read a book? Surely that's obvious – start at the beginning and keep going!' Yes, of course, if you are reading a novel. But a textbook is different. It is a mine of information, but it tells you more than you need to know to solve a particular problem. The art of using a textbook is to be selective. Look through the book to see how it breaks the subject down into chapters, sections and sub-sections. Make good use of the index, and do not be afraid to start reading in the middle of a chapter. To use an index sensibly, of course, you will need to look up significant words – 'keywords' – and, as we shall see, ILPAC can help you to do this.

So, let us suppose that you have found the right section of the textbook. What next? Well, read it and make a few notes. But is that advice as simple as it sounds? There are different ways of reading, and there are different ways of making notes. Let's look at this more closely.

■ Styles of reading

It is sometimes useful to divide methods of reading into three styles: scanning, skimming and intensive reading.

Scanning simply means running the eye rapidly down a page to search for particular words or phrases. To see how quickly you can scan a page, look up a word in the index of your textbook, say 'electron'. Turn to the first reference and look down the page so rapidly that the words are just a blur. Then slow down and look at the page again. Keep doing this, more slowly this time, until you can pick out the word you are looking for.

Skimming is slower than scanning and involves reading a passage to get an idea of its contents. Having skimmed through it, you should know whether or not the passage would repay closer study. If you cannot find what you want in one book by skimming, try another book.

Intensive reading means reading every word and studying the passage, sentence by sentence, until you have gained all the relevant information it contains.

Do remember that reading, at whatever depth, must be an active process. Be clear about what it is that you are looking for (ILPAC objectives are useful here – see below) and read for a purpose. It is quite possible to sit with glazed eyes at an open book and learn nothing!

■ Styles of note-taking

Your notes are for your benefit and so long as they are accurate and understandable by you, then they will serve their purpose. Two general points are worth making:

1. The better you have understood the material, the briefer will be your notes. They will then act as 'triggers' for your memory.
2. You should never copy out sections of text (except, perhaps, definitions and laws). Copied-out notes, neatly underlined, look reassuring but may be simply undigested material that you have not really thought about. There are at least two distinct styles of note-taking and these can be labelled 'linear' and 'patterned'.

Linear notes are ordered sequences of information, with headings and sub-headings.
Patterned notes are made by grouping words or phrases round a central idea.

To illustrate the differences between these two styles, some notes made on what has been written so far in this Introduction are shown opposite.

Whether you think these examples are particularly good notes does not really matter – that would be the concern of the students who wrote them. But do stop and ask yourself how you would have tackled the same job. Bear in mind that linear notes tend to be rather cut-and-dried (which may be appropriate) and that patterned notes are open-ended. You can always add to them and they encourage you to find connections between ideas that might not otherwise have occurred to you. In the end, however, you must develop whatever style suits you best – perhaps a combination of linear and patterned, depending upon the subject matter.

■ A reading strategy: SQR^3

Let us return to our first question – 'How should I study?' Research on how people learn shows that effective reading can be divided into stages. Here are five things you should do:

1. Survey the material you are going to read to get an overall view (e.g. scan the index and skim the more promising references).
2. Question yourself: 'Why am I doing this reading? What am I trying to find out?'
3. Read intensively the passages that you have chosen.
4. Recall: try to remember the main points from the passage you have just read. This may be an effort, but it is an important step in learning. Now is the time to make notes.
5. Review: check your notes against the passage to make sure that nothing important has been missed, and then look through your notes from time to time during the next day or two. Students who take two or three minutes to review notes within 24 hours of making them retain more of what they learn.

This reading strategy has been called, for short, SQR^3 (and sometimes SQ3R).

ILPAC Intro – Hints on study generally + ILPAC specifically

<u>A. How to Study.</u>

<u>1.</u> Copied notes not much good. Discourages <u>thinking</u> + <u>Independence</u>

<u>2.</u> <u>Textbooks.</u>
a) Look at Overall Structure
b) Use index - Keywords.
c) Scan - quick look to locate Keywords.
d) Skim — identify useful passages.
e) Intensive reading - thorough job.
f) <u>Active</u> reading. Read for a purpose.

<u>3.</u> <u>Notes</u>
a) Brief 'Triggers'
b) Don't copy chunks of text (except def's, Laws ?)
c) Linear notes - like these!
d) Patterned notes - web of linked ideas radiating from central theme.

<u>4.</u> . . . .
. . . . , ,

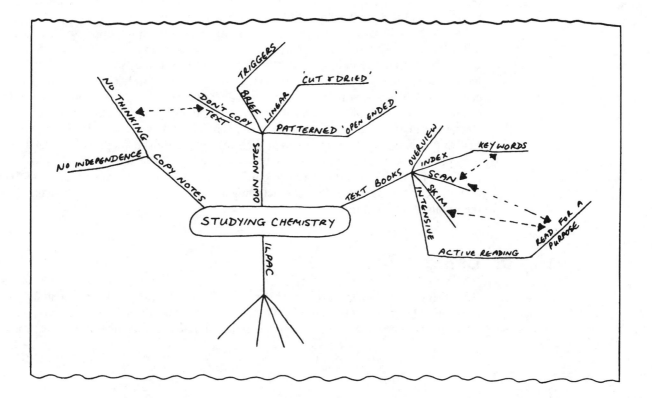

■ Time allocation for study

When to study You will benefit more from doing an hour or two each night than by trying to catch up at weekends or in holidays. Too much study in a single day only results in inefficient learning. Try to establish your own routine, setting aside a couple of hours each night, or at least on the nights when you've had chemistry that day. Don't forget your other subjects either!

Making study sessions effective Researchers have shown that we concentrate best for periods of 20–40 minutes without a break. After this time our attention wanders and studying efficiency falls off rapidly. So, give yourself a break every half hour or so – it may just be enough to get up and walk across the room or to have a chat with someone or look out of the window. Try to spend between one and three hours on a study session. If you find it difficult to get started, set yourself an easy task first, such as a short exercise. Getting this right will encourage you to carry on with the next task.

■ Resource-based learning

Books are essential, but are not the only sources of information. You can find out about chemistry in many ways – by watching films and television, by using computer programs, by making models, by visiting factories and laboratories and, of course, by doing experiments. These sources of information can be called resources. There is a further resource which must be added, perhaps the most important of all, the teacher. The contrast between resource-based learning and more traditional methods is conveniently illustrated by imagining two teachers at work.

The first, Mr A, is a traditionalist. He stands at the front of the class, explains the subject, gives full notes, asks questions and, once a week, supervises a practical lesson. Homework is set and marked but Mr A has such a lot of information to convey that he does not have much time to deal with individual difficulties. Because virtually all information comes through the teacher, the class moves forward together at the same steady pace. A few of the pupils find the pace too rapid and are having difficulties, but they prefer to sit quietly – it's embarrassing to hold up the rest by constantly asking questions. Others find the pace slow and are somewhat bored. Mr A's examination results are good, and all agree that he is an effective teacher.

Ms B is equally respected, and her results are also good but her approach is quite different. She is fond of saying 'Why should I tell you when you can find out for yourself?' At first, her pupils are a little disconcerted – but they soon realise that Ms B has not abandoned them. She has prepared what she calls 'Study Guides' – notes on each topic, with advice on what to read, what experiments to do, what difficulties to look out for, and so on. And, because she does not spend a great deal of time in lecturing the class, she can afford to deal with individual problems and to take part in discussions. Ms B's pupils can work more or less at their own pace, but she keeps a close watch on each person's progress, and no one is allowed to fall seriously behind. Ms B, who believes in resource-based learning, regards herself as a sort of manager; it is her job to make sure that the right resources (including her knowledge and skills) are available to the pupils at the right time.

■ Using ILPAC

ILPAC is designed to assist resource-based learning, sometimes called 'individualised learning'. The course was originally based on twenty units, each in its own book, but these units are now arranged in twelve volumes. These are not conventional textbooks, but study guides. The first three volumes form an essential starting block, because they contain material that you will need to use throughout the rest of the course, but various routes are possible thereafter. Your teacher will be able to advise you or give you a copy of suggested routes. However, some schools, and some individual students, select just some ILPAC units and integrate their use into a more conventional course of study.

Before you start working on your first unit, we suggest that you look quickly through the whole of it while reading the following notes on the main features you will find in it. This will give you an overview of the structure of a unit. You can then return to the notes later on when you reach a particular feature.

Symbols or headings in the margin will help you to find examples of each activity.

1. Pre-knowledge and pre-test

At the beginning of every unit we list, under the heading **Pre-knowledge**, some abilities which we assume you will have and which you will need to use later in the unit. Read the list and revise any topics if you think it is necessary or, if you think you have not covered a topic at all, consult your teacher. Then do the **Pre-test**, either on your own or, if your teacher prefers, in class. From the results, your teacher can tell whether you need to do any further revision before you begin the unit.

2. Parts

Most units are divided into two parts. Part A usually provides an introduction to the topic, while Part B takes you up to A-level standard. In some units, however, the parts simply divide the work into two subject areas. At the end of a unit you may find an Appendix and suggestions for further study.

3. Objectives and keywords

Objectives are statements, listed at the beginning of each section of study, which say what you should be able to do when you have finished that section. They are also a guide to important points to look for in your reading and contain emphasised 'keywords' to help you use the index of a textbook. You may also find keywords useful as a framework for making notes.

There may be some words or phrases in the objectives that are unfamiliar to you. Don't worry about this; at the end of the section you should understand them.

Your teacher should be able to give you a copy of all the objectives for a particular unit collected together in a checklist. For convenience we have condensed some of the objectives but we list them in the order in which they appear in the unit so that you can easily check your notes and use them to make summaries. Don't forget that some of the objectives will not be necessary for your particular syllabus; your teacher will advise you on this.

4. Reading

You will not find all the information you need in an ILPAC volume – we encourage you to study many topics by reading about them in textbooks and often give some guidance on points to look for and pitfalls to avoid. You should use the preceding objectives, especially the keywords, to help you find suitable passages to give purpose to your reading and to help you make notes. Here are some suggestions to help you in your reading:

1. Give yourself enough room to work – somewhere you can spread out your books and paper.
2. Go through the objectives listed above the reading task, noting the keywords. There may be some additional keywords in the reading task itself. Look up these keywords in the index of your textbook(s) and note the page numbers. If you cannot find what you want at first, try some alternative keywords – for instance, you might find 'atomic radius' under 'atom', 'radius' or 'size' or, in some indexes, under all three!

3. Turn to the page references for each objective and scan* each page in turn, looking for the keywords. In this way, identify sections that contain relevant information.
4. Skim* each of the sections you have identified, bearing in mind what you want to find out. You know this from the objectives, and also by looking at the exercises which come directly after the reading.
5. Read the passages intensively.*
6. Do the exercise(s) which follow the reading. These are designed to test your understanding of what you have just read, so you may find that you need to re-read the passage. If you still can't find what you want, you may have missed something in the index to refer you to another passage. You may even have to try another textbook!
7. Having done the exercises, look back at the objectives. Do they include anything not covered by the exercises? If so, make a note of the missing items and if you are still not happy about them when you have gone a little further, try again to find what you need in your textbook.

5. Exercises

There are numerous exercises throughout the course to help you check your progress and to give you practice in applying what you have just learned. One of the main features of ILPAC is the provision of detailed answers to all these exercises at the end of each volume. Some of the exercises (and some of the questions in the tests) are similar to questions you might encounter in an A-level examination, and the detailed answers will show you what an A-level examiner might expect to see in your answer script. These questions are identified by symbols in the margin.

Where a question is taken from a past examination paper, the examination board and the year are identified in the acknowledgements section at the beginning of the unit.

6. Worked Examples

Throughout the course, we explain calculations by means of Worked Examples. Reading carefully through a Worked Example should enable you to do the exercise(s) which follow it, although you may have to look again. If that fails, look at the method in the answer to the exercise, and then have another try. If this does not help, ask your teacher.

Don't be casual about calculations – write out every step of the solution so that it would make sense to a fellow student (and to you when you revise!) and be sure to include units. In an examination, a clearly set out method will not only help you to solve the problem correctly but will also gain you most of the marks if a simple identifiable slip leads you to a wrong answer.

Significant figures are important, and you will normally be expected to round off your answers to three significant figures, unless otherwise stated. You should look at Appendix 2 to The Mole unit of Volume 1 if you need help in understanding how to handle significant figures. A-level examiners have become increasingly strict on this and you will almost certainly be penalised if you write down your complete calculator display as an answer with no attempt to estimate significant figures correctly.

7. Teacher-marked Exercises

Teacher-marked Exercises are designed to give you practice in essay-type questions and to help your teacher to monitor your progress. Before you start one, look back at your notes on the topic to make sure you are clear about the main points, then read the question again, carefully, to make sure you answer **that** question and not a similar one with a rather different emphasis. You should try to make your answer 'fit the question' and avoid the temptation to just churn out everything you can remember about the topic, in random order! With this in mind, and with notes and textbooks closed, make a

---

*'Scanning', 'skimming' and 'intensive reading' were explained earlier in this Introduction. Look back at this if you are not sure what we mean by these terms.

short plan of your answer. Spend about half an hour writing and then hand your full answer, together with your plan, to your teacher for marking. We do not provide a specimen answer because there is nearly always more than one acceptable way to tackle the question.

8. Revealing Exercises

Also included in some of the units are Revealing Exercises, which lead you step by step, in a logical sequence of short questions and answers, through some more difficult or lengthy concepts. To start this type of exercise you cover up, with a blank sheet of paper, all but the first question. Think about an answer, and preferably write it down, before moving your blank paper down the page to reveal the given answer, and the next question. Then repeat the procedure to the end.

9. Experiments

Experiments are integrated into the course and have a variety of functions in the ILPAC scheme: some are designed to help you develop essential practical skills, while others illustrate theoretical points. There are also opportunities for you to plan your own experimental work – valuable for all students and essential for those being tested for examination purpose by practical assessments.

Ideally you should do each experiment at the time you reach it in the text, but you may have to plan ahead in order to make best use of limited laboratory time, or to ensure that the necessary equipment is made available for you.

Make sure that you have time to do the experiment and that your teacher knows that you are about to do it. You should not do practical work if your teacher is not present at the time. Also make sure that you understand the purpose of the experiment; this is stated in the Aim. The Introduction gives information needed for the experiment. Pay attention to any **hazard warnings** – these advise you on the dangers of handling certain chemicals. If you are told to wear safety spectacles or use a fume cupboard, then you **must** do so. Follow instructions carefully, making sure that you use the correct substances in the stated quantities. If laboratory time is scarce, complete the experiment before doing calculations – then you can write up the experiment at home.

Most A-level examinations include a practical test or a practical assessment by the teacher, and a written record of your work will help you achieve a suitable standard. We now give detailed suggestions for writing up experiments carefully after completing them, using most of the headings we use in the unit.

Title and aim These will be the same as in the unit.

Procedure Our instructions have to be very detailed: your account should be much briefer, more like our introduction but with enough detail added to remind you of the method.

Results tables These are designed to help you record data in a form which you can use easily. Get used to recording results clearly as you work – scribbled figures on scraps of paper can be confusing even if you don't lose them! Your teacher may be able to give you duplicated blank tables.

Calculations You must include enough explanation to enable you to follow the calculations when you revise. A couple of lines of scribbled figures with no indication of method is quite useless. Our specimen calculations are a good guide.

Questions We include these to help you understand the method and its limitations. Your answers should therefore be useful in revision. Either copy out the questions or write your answer in such a way that the question is also included. Avoid answers beginning 'Because . . . ' – they are likely to be grammatically incorrect and are not at all helpful in revision unless the question is stated.

Comment Finish your account with a comment on the accuracy of your results and, if they are poor, some indication of the probable reasons.

10. Video programmes

A series of video-cassettes (VHS) has been made to accompany the units. You should find them very helpful but, if they are not available, you can still follow ILPAC without them. Your teacher has a list of the videos.

Before you watch a programme, find out how long it lasts and whether there is time to see it more than once and/or to stop it at convenient points for note-taking and discussion. Have a pen and paper ready because you are often asked to record data during a programme.

If you have time, it is a good idea to watch a programme straight through first, and then make notes on the points you want to remember during a second showing.

11. Computer programs

There are many educational computer programs, available commercially or through teachers' centres, which may be relevant to some topics in your course, particularly the more mathematical ones. They introduce some variety to your activities and may help you to understand some ideas better. However, as with the videos, you can still follow ILPAC without them.

We no longer recommend specific programs because new and updated programs are being released all the time. Also, some of those we might recommend were written for a particular computer and might not work on the machines available to you. Your teacher should have a list of resources and be able to help you choose suitable programs.

12. Model-making

Making three-dimensional models of molecules and giant structures can be very helpful in interpreting two-dimensional diagrams in books. For some people, it is the **only** way to understand fully how shapes of molecules and bond angles affect the course of chemical reactions. This can be most important in your study òf organic chemistry.

13. Data book

You will refer frequently to your data book throughout this course so you must learn how to use it effectively.

For example, you may be asked to use your data book to calculate molar masses. Turn to the index and find the page reference(s) for molar mass or relative atomic mass. If there is more than one reference, look at them all and see which is most convenient for your purpose. A table which gives very precise values may be confusing if you only need approximate values. Is it easier to have the elements listed alphabetically or by atomic number?

Always look carefully at the headings of columns in tables of data, and read any accompanying notes to make sure that the data are really what you want and that you quote the correct units.

14. Tests (End-of-part and End-of-unit)

After your revision, based on the checklist of objectives (see above), attempt the test at the end of each part. The test is designed to show **you** what you should have learned and to help your teacher to monitor your progress. Where appropriate, A-level questions are included.

If your teacher agrees, you could do the test at home but resist the temptation to study the questions, and observe the rules – only you will lose out if you cheat!

15. End-of-unit summary

It is a good idea to summarise the contents of each unit on a **single sheet** of paper. Look again at the section on note-taking at the beginning of this Introduction to ILPAC.

Symbols used in ILPAC

 Computer program

 Discussion

 Experiment

 Model-making

 Reading

 Revealing Exercise

 Video programme

 A- level question

 A-level part question

 A-level question; Special Paper

 A-level supplementary question

International hazard symbols

 Corrosive

 Explosive

Harmful or irritant

Highly flammable

 Oxidising

 Radioactive

Toxic

CHEMICAL ENERGETICS

INTRODUCTION

All chemical reactions involve energy changes. For example, your school or college is heated by burning natural gas, oil, coal or coke, either close at hand or in a power station; you have probably noticed a rise in temperature when an acid reacts with an alkali in a test-tube; the metabolism of food releases energy that is needed to 'drive' other vital reactions in your body.

The study of energy changes is an important part of chemistry. Fundamental to the study of energetics is the law of conservation of energy, which states that energy is neither created nor destroyed, but can be converted from one form to another. Such transformations account for heat from the burning of coal being able to turn a turbine to generate electricity, and the changes in potential energy and kinetic energy when a ball is thrown up into the air.

In this volume we are particularly concerned with the transformation of chemical energy (energy stored in every chemical substance) into heat energy, and vice versa. By the end of the volume you should have some understanding of the relationship between chemical energy and chemical bonds.

In Part A we extend many of the ideas of energetics from your pre-A-level course and introduce Hess' law, an application of the law of conservation of energy, which enables you to calculate some energy changes that cannot be measured directly. We also show you how the energy (enthalpy) changes associated with chemical reactions are used to discuss the stability of substances and the likelihood of those reactions occurring spontaneously.

In Part B we look more closely at the energetics of bond formation in both covalent and ionic substances. To enable you to predict more reliably the possibility of a reaction occurring, we introduce you to two more thermodynamic quantities, free energy and entropy, and show how they are related to enthalpy.

There are six experiments in this volume, but you may not have time to do them all. Three are in Part A, two in Part B and one in the Appendix.

There is an ILPAC video programme designed to accompany this volume. It is not essential, but you should try to see it at the appropriate time if it is available.

Using a heat of combustion apparatus.

■ Pre-knowledge

Before you start work on this book you should be able to:

1. Do simple calculations of reacting mass based on chemical equations.
2. Define 'heat capacity' and 'specific heat capacity'.
3. Calculate the heat capacity of an object of uniform composition (e.g. all glass, all copper, all solution) using the relationship:

$$\textbf{heat capacity} = \textbf{mass} \times \textbf{specific heat capacity}$$

usual units: $kJ\ K^{-1}$ kg $kJ\ kg^{-1}\ K^{-1}$

                (or $J\ K^{-1}$ or g   or $J\ g^{-1}\ K^{-1}$)

4. Calculate the heat gained or lost by an object (i.e. its change in heat energy) when its temperature changes, using the relationship:

$$\textbf{heat gain or loss} = \textbf{heat capacity} \times \textbf{temperature change}$$

usual units: kJ $kJ\ K^{-1}$ K

5. Solve simple simultaneous equations in x and y.

■ Pre-test

To find out whether you are ready to start Part A try the following test, which is based on the pre-knowledge items. You should not spend more than 40 minutes on this test. Hand your answers to your teacher for marking.

1. What mass of lead would be obtained on complete reduction of 1.60 g of lead(IV) oxide by hydrogen?

$$PbO_2 \text{ (s)} + 2H_2 \text{ (g)} \rightarrow Pb \text{ (s)} + 2H_2O \text{ (g)} \qquad (4)$$

2. From the equation

$$CuSO_4 \text{ (s)} + 100H_2O \text{ (l)} \rightarrow CuSO_4 \text{ (aq, } 100H_2O)$$

calculate the masses of copper sulphate and water required to prepare the solution from 0.025 mol of the solid. (4)

3. State, in your own words, what you understand by the terms:
   a heat capacity of an object,
   b specific heat capacity of a substance. (4)

4. When one mole of concentrated sulphuric acid is carefully added to sufficient water to make 1 dm^3 of solution, the temperature of the solution rises by 17°C. Calculate the increase in heat energy of the solution. You may assume in your calculation that the specific heat capacity of the mixture is the same as that of water, 4.2 kJ kg^{-1} K^{-1}, and that 1 dm^3 of water weighs 1 kg. (2)

5. A copper can (calorimeter) of mass 60 g containing 100 g of water was heated by a spirit lamp until the temperature of the water rose by 10°C. Calculate the heat energy transferred from the flame to the calorimeter and contents. (Specific heat capacities: water, 4.18 kJ kg^{-1} K^{-1}; copper, 0.38 kJ kg^{-1} K^{-1}.) (4)

6. Solve the simultaneous equations:
$$3x + 2y = 16$$
$$2x + y = 9$$
   (2)
   (Total: 20 marks)

We start this volume by defining some important terms used in the study of energetics, sometimes called thermodynamics. The subject was developed in the nineteenth century, so some of the words may seem strange. They will, of course, eventually form an integral part of your scientific vocabulary.

CHAPTER

BASIC IDEAS

When you read your textbooks you may find it assumed that certain terms and ideas are familiar to you. In the following sections we briefly describe and define them to aid your reading.

OBJECTIVES When you have finished this chapter you should be able to:
- distinguish between **system** and **surroundings**;
- describe a process as **exothermic** or **endothermic**;
- describe in principle how **enthalpy changes** are measured;
- quote the **standard conditions** for thermodynamic processes.

■ 1.1 System and surroundings

In your study of energetics (and, later, of chemical equilibrium), you must define the region or particular quantity of matter of interest. This is called the **system**. Two examples are:

a One in which no reaction is taking place; e.g. 25 g of potassium bromide under different physical conditions (see Fig. 1).

Figure 1
The same system under different conditions.

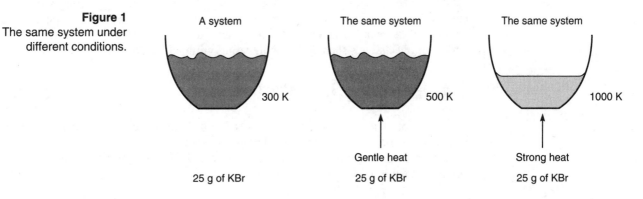

A system   The same system   The same system

300 K   500 K   1000 K

Gentle heat   Strong heat

25 g of KBr   25 g of KBr   25 g of KBr

b One in which reaction could take place, or is taking place, or has taken place; e.g. stoichiometric amounts of magnesium and hydrochloric acid (see Fig. 2).

Figure 2
A system in which a reaction
occurs.

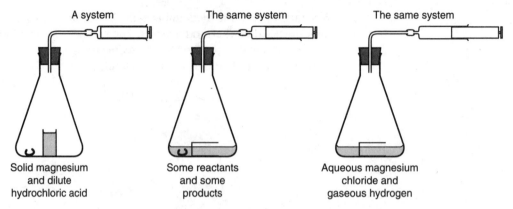

The surroundings are everything other than the system. In certain instances it is important to specify whether the container (e.g. the crucible in Fig. 1 or the flask and syringe in Fig. 2) is to be considered part of the system or part of the surroundings.

■ 1.2 The symbol Δ (Greek letter 'delta')

In science and mathematics we use the symbol Δ to indicate an **increase** in a quantity; for example, an increase in temperature from 295 to 300 K may be referred to as ΔT, where

$$\Delta T = T(\text{final}) - T(\text{initial})$$
$$= 300 \text{ K} - 295 \text{ K} = 5 \text{ K}$$

A negative value of ΔT implies a **decrease** in temperature. However, you may find the symbol Δ used to refer to a **change** in a quantity, X, in such a way that both increases and decreases are positive. But remember, the strict definition of ΔX is

$$\Delta X = X(\text{final}) - X(\text{initial})$$

■ 1.3 Exothermic and endothermic changes

An exothermic change is one in which stored chemical energy is converted to heat energy. We often say that 'heat is given out' (the prefix 'ex-' means 'out' – as in 'exit') or 'heat is released' or 'heat is evolved'. This heat energy very often increases the temperature of the system, and then is transferred to the surroundings as the temperature returns to normal. You are familiar with exothermic changes such as the burning of fuel and the condensation of water vapour (this is why steam can cause more severe scalding than water at the same temperature).

Conversely, an endothermic change is one in which heat energy is converted to chemical energy. Heat energy is absorbed, and this can cause a fall in temperature of the system unless heat is transferred from the surroundings. You are familiar with endothermic changes such as dissolving ammonium chloride in water or frying an egg.

■ 1.4 Enthalpy (symbol *H*)

The enthalpy of a substance, sometimes called its heat content, is an indication of its total energy content. The name 'heat content' is quite helpful because it changes by heat energy passing in or out. We shall not attempt to define enthalpy formally, and we cannot measure it, but we can measure enthalpy **changes** and these are very useful.

A simple analogy may be helpful here: if you are out walking in the hills you probably do not worry much about your height above sea level, but it is easy to tell whether you are going up or down, and information on differences in height is very useful in planning your journey. In just the same way, enthalpy changes are much more important than enthalpy itself.

■ 1.5 Enthalpy change, ΔH

There are two main ways in which the enthalpy of a system can change. One is by a change in temperature corresponding to a change in heat energy; for instance, 25 g of water at 70°C has a greater enthalpy than 25 g of water at 50°C. The other is by a change in chemical energy, or stored energy; for instance, 25 g of water vapour at 100°C has a greater enthalpy than 25 g of liquid water at 100°C.

In each of these cases, it is possible to measure ΔH by measuring the heat energy input required to make the change.

In chemical reactions, both types of enthalpy change are likely to occur, but in order to focus attention on chemical energy we usually measure enthalpy changes between reactants and products which are at **the same temperature**.

Changes in pressure and volume also have some bearing on the way we describe energy changes, as we now show.

■ 1.6 The constant pressure process

Consider the reaction between magnesium and hydrochloric acid:

$$Mg\ (s) + 2HCl\ (aq) \rightarrow MgCl_2\ (aq) + H_2\ (g)$$

Assume that the reaction is carried out in the apparatus in Fig. 3(a) under the laboratory conditions shown.

Figure 3
Chemical reaction at constant pressure.

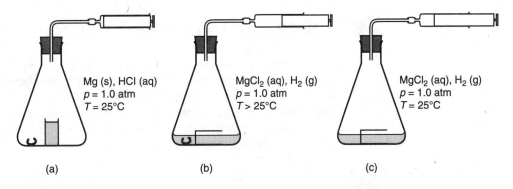

Mg (s), HCl (aq)
$p = 1.0$ atm
$T = 25°C$

(a)

MgCl$_2$ (aq), H$_2$ (g)
$p = 1.0$ atm
$T > 25°C$

(b)

MgCl$_2$ (aq), H$_2$ (g)
$p = 1.0$ atm
$T = 25°C$

(c)

We allow the two to react, and immediately after reaction we have the situation shown in Fig. 3(b), where the temperature has increased due to heat energy released in the reaction.

Then we let the system cool back to room temperature (25°C). Its final state is described in Fig. 3(c).

Notice that both before and after the reaction the temperature and pressure are the same but the volume is different.

If we measure all the heat transferred between system and surroundings in order to return the system to 25°C, this is the **enthalpy change** for the reaction.

Most reactions you study are carried out at constant pressure, but sometimes you may consider a process where the pressure may vary because the volume is kept constant.

■ 1.7 The constant volume process

We can perform this same reaction at constant volume in a very strong flask. Again, we assume a set of initial conditions and let the substances react as before. After an intermediate state when all the magnesium has reacted and the temperature is greater than 25°C, the system cools back to 25°C, but the pressure is higher than before. The process is shown in Fig. 4.

Figure 4
Chemical reaction at constant volume.

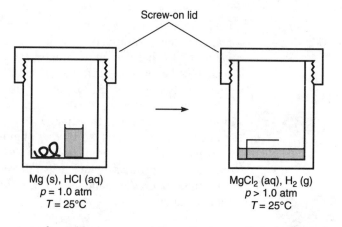

Screw-on lid

Mg (s), HCl (aq)
$p = 1.0$ atm
$T = 25°C$

MgCl$_2$ (aq), H$_2$ (g)
$p > 1.0$ atm
$T = 25°C$

The heat energy transferred between system and surroundings is **not** quite the same as the enthalpy change, ΔH: it is a true measure of the change in internal energy, ΔU. In many cases, there is very little difference between ΔH and ΔU. In Appendix 2, we show the relation between enthalpy change and internal energy change. Ask your teacher if you should study this.

All of the reactions you perform in the laboratory are constant pressure processes because they take place in open containers. Therefore we concentrate on enthalpy changes, especially those which occur under certain standard conditions.

■ 1.8 Standard enthalpy change, $\Delta H^\ominus$

For the basis of comparison and tabulation of data, a set of standard conditions has been arbitrarily defined for thermodynamics; the enthalpy change for a reaction which occurs at a pressure of 100 kPa (1 atm) and 298 K (25°C) is called the standard enthalpy change and is indicated by the symbol $\Delta H^\ominus$ (298 K). Usually, however, the '298 K' is omitted. If the temperature is other than this, it is indicated. Standard conditions also imply that all substances are in their 'standard states' (the most stable in the conditions), e.g. H$_2$O (l) not H$_2$O (g) at 1 atm and 298 K.

Now that we have given a rather lengthy introduction to enthalpy change, you should see what your textbooks have to say on the subject. Look in the index under **enthalpy change** or **heat of reaction**. (Note that the terms 'enthalpy change', 'energy change', and 'heat' are often used interchangeably in this context.) You should then be able to do the following exercises.

EXERCISE 1
Answer on page 80

State the temperature, pressure and concentration which are the thermodynamic standard conditions.

EXERCISE 2
Answers on page 80

a Classify the following changes as exothermic or endothermic.
  i) Sodium hydroxide dissolves in water and the temperature of the solution rises.
  ii) Ammonium chloride dissolves in water and the temperature of the surroundings drops.
  iii) Hydrogen and oxygen combine explosively to form water.

iv) Liquid water condenses to ice at 0°C.

v) Liquid nitrogen (boiling point = 77 K) boils spontaneously at room temperature.

b Explain why $\Delta H^{\ominus}$ has a negative value for an exothermic reaction and a positive value for an endothermic reaction.

It is very convenient to link values of standard enthalpy change with chemical equations, which we now consider.

■ 1.9 Thermochemical equations

A thermochemical equation summarises the information needed in the study of energetics – it gives the amounts, measured in moles, of reactants and products, and also tells the quantity of energy involved. One such equation is given below. It summarises these facts: when two moles of hydrogen react with one mole of oxygen to produce two moles of liquid water, with both initial and final states at 298 K and 1 atm, 572 kJ of heat energy are released to the surroundings

$$2H_2\ (g) + O_2\ (g) \rightarrow 2H_2O\ (l); \quad \Delta H^{\ominus} = -572 \text{ kJ mol}^{-1}$$

Notice the use of the symbol $^{\ominus}$ to indicate standard conditions. If half the amounts are used, then the energy is halved also.

$$H_2\ (g) + \tfrac{1}{2}O_2\ (g) \rightarrow H_2O\ (l); \quad \Delta H^{\ominus} = -286 \text{ kJ mol}^{-1}$$

Notice that in both examples, the unit for the standard enthalpy change is kJ mol^{-1}. You can consider that the term 'per mole' refers to all the amounts specified in the equation. You may find it useful to think of the term 'per mole' as referring to 'a mole of equation' if, as in the two examples, the stoichiometric coefficients are not all unity.

It is important to include the state symbols (e.g. g, l, s, aq) because the energy change depends on the state of the substance. If the water produced were not allowed to condense, then we would write a thermochemical equation with a different value of the enthalpy change

$$2H_2\ (g) + O_2\ (g) \rightarrow 2H_2O\ (g); \quad \Delta H^{\ominus} = -484 \text{ kJ mol}^{-1}$$

Another useful way to summarise thermochemical data is to use energy-level diagrams.

■ 1.10 Energy-level diagrams

An energy-level diagram drawn to scale provides a way to visualise the relative enthalpies of substances in a reaction (or process).

OBJECTIVES When you have finished this section you should be able to:
- ■ relate thermochemical equations to **energy-level diagrams**;
- ■ use an energy-level diagram to calculate enthalpy change.

We introduce energy-level diagrams by a Worked Example.

WORKED EXAMPLE Consider the two thermochemical equations:

$$2H_2\ (g) + O_2\ (g) \rightarrow 2H_2O\ (g); \quad \Delta H^{\ominus} = -484 \text{ kJ mol}^{-1}$$

$$2H_2\ (g) + O_2\ (g) \rightarrow 2H_2O\ (l); \quad \Delta H^{\ominus} = -572 \text{ kJ mol}^{-1}$$

Draw an energy-level diagram to represent both of these changes.

Solution   1. We plot enthalpy vertically and specify the scale. Here let 1 cm = 200 kJ mol^{-1}. Draw a horizontal line to represent the enthalpy of the reactants. It is quite proper to do this even though we do not know where zero enthalpy is.

H | $2H_2$ (g) + O_2 (g)

2. Measure the distance downward corresponding to the release of 484 kJ mol^{-1} of energy and draw another horizontal line to indicate the enthalpy of 2 mol of gaseous water. The arrow shows the direction of change, as does the negative sign.

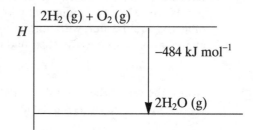

3. Measure the distance downward from the first line corresponding to the release of 572 kJ mol^{-1} of energy and draw a third horizontal line to show the enthalpy of 2 mol of liquid water.

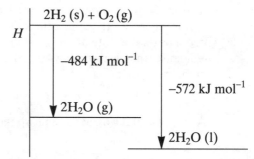

Now try the next exercise based on this diagram.

EXERCISE 3
Answer on page 80

How much heat is released when one mole of steam condenses to one mole of liquid water? Write a thermochemical equation summarising this information.

The next exercises emphasise the use of thermochemical equations and energy-level diagrams.

EXERCISE 4
Answers on page 80

When one mole of graphite is burned completely in oxygen to produce carbon dioxide, 394 kJ of heat is evolved whereas, when diamond is similarly burned, 396 kJ is evolved.
a Write thermochemical equations summarising this information.
b Draw an energy-level diagram comparing the combustion of diamond and graphite.
c What is the enthalpy change for the conversion of graphite into diamond?

EXERCISE 5
Answers on page 80

Draw energy-level diagrams for the following reactions:

a C (s) + 2S (s) → CS_2 (l); $\Delta H^\circ = +88$ kJ mol^{-1}

b Zn (s) + $2H^+$ (aq) → Zn^{2+} (aq) + H_2 (g); $\Delta H^\circ = -152$ kJ mol^{-1}

EXERCISE 6

Answer on page 81

The two energy-level diagrams below refer to the complete combustion, under standard conditions, of 1 mol of carbon when mixed with different amounts of oxygen.

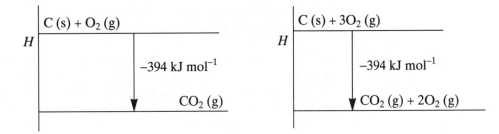

Explain why the two additional moles of oxygen do not affect the enthalpy change.

Since the enthalpy change in the last exercise refers to combustion, it is sometimes called enthalpy change of combustion or, more simply, heat of combustion. Enthalpy changes for other types of reaction may be named in a similar way.

■ 1.11 Labelling enthalpy changes

In order to tabulate numerical values of standard enthalpy change, certain types of reaction and their enthalpy changes are labelled. For example, standard enthalpy change of formation (symbol: $\Delta H_f^\ominus$); standard enthalpy change of combustion (symbol: $\Delta H_c^\ominus$) and standard enthalpy change of solution (symbol: $\Delta H_{soln}^\ominus$). Note that the word 'standard' is sometimes omitted but is always implied by the symbol $^\ominus$. The word 'change' is also often omitted.

OBJECTIVES

When you have finished this section you should be able to:
■ define **a enthalpy change of formation,**
        b enthalpy change of combustion,
        c enthalpy change of solution;
■ use your data book to find numerical values of these enthalpy changes;
■ recognise that the standard enthalpy change of formation of an element in its standard state is defined as zero.

Look up the definitions of different types of enthalpy change in your textbook(s). Include examples in your notes. Remember that, for example, 'standard enthalpy change of combustion' may be shortened to 'enthalpy of combustion' or even 'heat of combustion'.

To see if you can apply these definitions, do the next two exercises.

EXERCISE 7

Answers on page 81

a Select the specific term(s) which describe the enthalpy changes in the following reactions:
   i) $C_2H_5OH\ (l) + 3O_2\ (g) \rightarrow 2CO_2\ (g) + 3H_2O\ (l)$
   ii) $CuSO_4\ (s) + 100H_2O\ (l) \rightarrow CuSO_4\ (aq, 100H_2O)$
   iii) $Mg\ (s) + \frac{1}{2}O_2\ (g) \rightarrow MgO\ (s)$
   iv) $H_2\ (g) + \frac{1}{2}O_2\ (g) \rightarrow H_2O\ (l)$
   v) $S\ (s) + O_2\ (g) \rightarrow SO_2\ (g)$

b Using your data book, list the numerical value of the enthalpy change in each of these reactions.

EXERCISE 8

Answers on page 81

Write complete thermochemical equations showing
a the standard heat of combustion of methane, CH_4,
b the standard enthalpy change of formation of calcium oxide, CaO,
c the standard heat of formation of liquid bromine, Br_2,
d the standard heat of formation of sodium metal, Na.

As stated on page 9, the amounts of reactants determine the quantity of heat which is exchanged with the surroundings. The enthalpy change of formation of one mole of water is -285.9 kJ mol^{-1} and for two moles of water it is twice this amount, -571.8 kJ mol^{-1}. To avoid confusion in such cases, an equation should always be written, as in the next two exercises.

EXERCISE 9

Answers on page 81

Write thermochemical equations to represent the following reactions at standard conditions:
a the combustion of 2.00 mol of calcium,
b the formation of 1.00 mol of ammonia from its elements,
c the dissolving of 1.00 mol of magnesium chloride in 500 mol of water,
d the combustion of 1.00 mol of ethane, C_2H_6.

EXERCISE 10

Answers on page 81

a Write a thermochemical equation showing that when 1.00 mol of carbon burns completely in oxygen, 394 kJ of heat is liberated.
b Calculate the enthalpy change on complete combustion of
  i) 10.0 mol of carbon,
  ii) 0.25 mol of carbon,
  iii) 18.0 g of carbon.
c What mass of carbon would have to be burned to produce
  i) 197 kJ,
  ii) 1000 kJ?

For convenience, we can use a shorthand notation. For example, 'the standard enthalpy change of formation of water is -286 kJ mol^{-1}' can be represented as

$$\Delta H_f^{\ominus}[H_2O\ (l)] = -286 \text{ kJ mol}^{-1}.$$

Similarly, for the standard heat of combustion of hydrogen, we can write

$$\Delta H_c^{\ominus}[H_2\ (g)] = -286 \text{ kJ mol}^{-1}.$$

Now that you understand what enthalpy changes are, we consider practical ways of measuring them.

EXPERIMENTAL DETERMINATION OF ENTHALPY CHANGE

In discussing enthalpy changes earlier, we spoke of heat transfers to the surroundings and of being able to measure them. In practice, it is much easier to measure the enthalpy change of a reaction using a calorimeter in which the system is insulated from the surroundings. For an exothermic reaction, the energy that would otherwise be given to the surroundings results in an increase in the temperature of the system.

If the maximum temperature change of the system is recorded and if the heat capacity of the system is known, it is easy to calculate the quantity of heat which would have to be taken from the system in order to restore it to its initial temperature. This quantity of heat is the enthalpy change. The sequence is summarised in Fig. 5.

Figure 5
Measuring ΔH for an exothermic reaction.

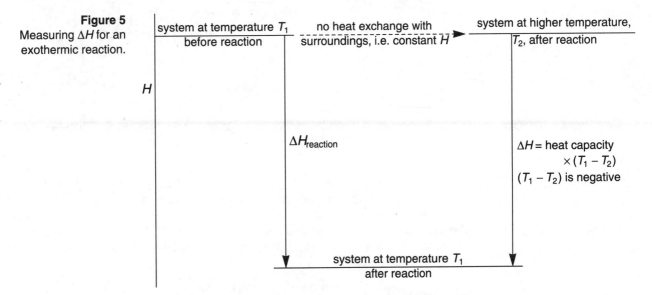

For an endothermic reaction, the temperature of the system would drop, but again the enthalpy change can be calculated from the temperature change if the heat capacity of the system is known. In this case the sequence is summarised in Fig. 6

Figure 6
Measuring ΔH for an endothermic reaction.

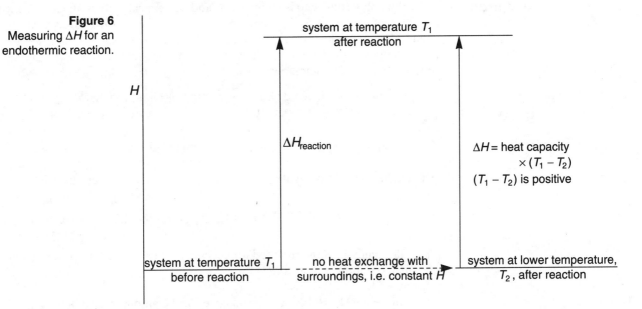

There are several types of insulated calorimeter you can use for simple experiments, as illustrated in Fig. 7. These calorimeters insulate the system from the surroundings so that all energy changes occur within the system. The energy exchanged with the surroundings is usually small enough to be ignored.

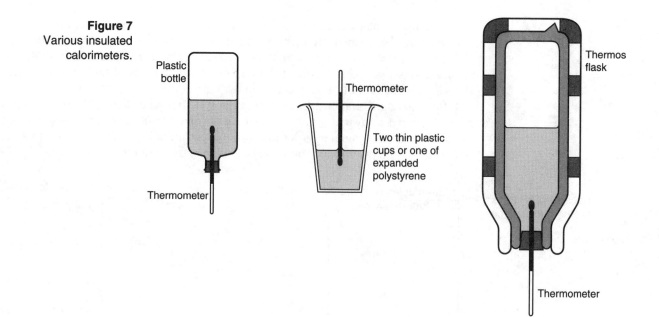

Figure 7
Various insulated calorimeters.

Before you begin Experiment 1, we give a Worked Example showing how the enthalpy change of reaction can be calculated from experimental data.

WORKED EXAMPLE

An excess of zinc powder was added to 50.0 cm³ of 0.100 M AgNO₃ in a polystyrene cup. Initially, the temperature was 21.10°C and it rose to 25.40°C. Calculate the enthalpy change for the reaction:

$$Zn\ (s) + 2Ag^+\ (aq) \rightarrow Zn^{2+}\ (aq) + 2Ag\ (s)$$

Assume that the density of the solution is 1.00 g cm⁻³ and its specific heat capacity is 4.18 kJ kg⁻¹ K⁻¹. Ignore the heat capacity of the metals.

Solution

1. Since the polystyrene cup is an insulator and its heat capacity is almost zero, you can assume that no energy is exchanged between system and surroundings. All the chemical energy released in the reaction is transformed into heat energy which raises the temperature of the solution. This energy must be removed in restoring the solution to the original temperature.

$$\begin{bmatrix} \text{enthalpy change,} \Delta H, \text{due} \\ \text{to reaction (at constant } T) \end{bmatrix} = \begin{bmatrix} \text{enthalpy change in restoring} \\ \text{solution to original temperature} \end{bmatrix}$$

$$= \begin{bmatrix} \text{mass} \times \text{specific heat capacity} \times \text{temperature change} \end{bmatrix} = mc_p{}^* \Delta T$$

(Remember that ΔT is negative in restoring the original temperature)

$$\therefore \Delta H = mc_p \Delta T = \frac{50.0}{1000}\,\text{kg} \times 4.18\ \text{kJ kg}^{-1}\ \text{K}^{-1} \times (-4.30\ \text{K}) = -0.899\ \text{kJ}$$

[*c_p is the symbol commonly used for specific heat capacity. The 'p' refers to constant pressure conditions (as does ΔH).]

2. The value −0.899 kJ is the enthalpy change for the amounts used in the experiment. To obtain a value for the enthalpy change of reaction, compare the amounts used in the experiment with the amounts shown in the equation:

$$Zn\ (s) + 2Ag^+\ (aq) \rightarrow Zn^{2+}\ (aq) + Ag\ (s)$$
1 mol   2 mol

The amount of silver ions used = $0.0500 \text{ dm}^3 \times 0.100 \text{ mol dm}^{-3} = 5.00 \times 10^{-3} \text{ mol}$

∴ the enthalpy change using 2 mol of Ag^+

$$= -0.899 \text{ kJ} \times \frac{2.00 \text{ mol}}{5.00 \times 10^{-3} \text{ mol}} = -360 \text{ kJ}$$

3. Now write the complete thermochemical equation:

Zn (s) + $2Ag^+$ (aq) → Zn^{2+} (aq) + Ag (s); $\Delta H = -360 \text{ kJ mol}^{-1}$.

Strictly speaking, you should not write $\Delta H^{\ominus}$ in this case because the conditions of the experiment were not standard, but the values of ΔH and $\Delta H^{\ominus}$ would be very close.

Note that enthalpy changes related to equations, which include all standard enthalpy changes, have the unit kJ mol^{-1}, where mol^{-1} means 'per mole of whatever is written in the equation'. For example, in step 3 above, mol^{-1} refers to a mole of units, **each** consisting of one zinc atom and two silver ions.

Now you can do an experiment which is similar to the one described in the Worked Example.

EXPERIMENT 1 Determining an enthalpy change of reaction

Aim The purpose of this experiment is to determine the enthalpy change for the displacement reaction:

Zn (s) + Cu^{2+} (aq) → Cu (s) + Zn^{2+} (aq)

Introduction By adding an excess of zinc powder to a measured amount of aqueous copper(II) sulphate, and measuring the temperature change over a period of time, you can then calculate the enthalpy change for the reaction.

Requirements
- safety spectacles
- pipette, 25 cm^3
- pipette filler
- polystyrene cup with lid
- copper(II) sulphate solution, 1.00 M CuSO$_4$ (harmful if swallowed)
- weighing bottle
- spatula
- zinc powder
- balance
- thermometer, 0–100°C (0.1° graduations)
- watch or clock with second hand

Procedure
1. Pipette 25.0 cm^3 of the copper(II) sulphate solution into a polystyrene cup.
2. Weigh about 6 g of zinc powder in the weighing bottle. Since this is an excess, there is no need to be accurate.
3. Put the thermometer through the hole in the lid, stir and record the temperature to the nearest 0.1°C every half minute for 2½ minutes.
4. At precisely 3 minutes, add the zinc powder to the cup.
5. Continue stirring and record the temperature for an additional 6 minutes to complete a copy of Results Table 1.

Results Table 1

Time/min	0.0	0.5	1.0	1.5	2.0	2.5	3.0	3.5	4.0	4.5
Temperature/°C							–			
Time/min	5.0	5.5	6.0	6.5	7.0	7.5	8.0	8.5	9.0	9.5
Temperature/°C										

Calculations

Specimen results on page 82

1. Plot the temperature (*y*-axis) against time (*x*-axis).
2. Extrapolate the curve to 3.0 minutes to establish the maximum temperature rise as shown in Fig. 8.

Figure 8

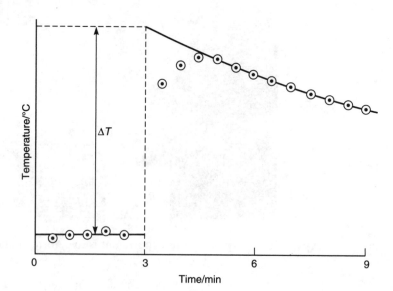

3. Calculate the enthalpy change for the quantities used, making the same assumptions as in the preceding exercise.
4. Calculate the enthalpy change for one mole of Zn and CuSO$_4$ (aq), and write the thermochemical equation for the reaction.

Questions

Answers on page 83

1. Compare your result with the accepted value of -217 kJ mol^{-1} by calculating the percentage error in your answer:

$$\text{error} = \frac{\text{experimental value} - \text{accepted value}}{\text{accepted value}} \times 100\%$$

2. List possible reasons for any difference between your value and the accepted value.
3. Why do you think the temperature increases for a few readings after adding the zinc? (Hint: it does **not** increase if a large excess of zinc is used or if the powder is very finely divided.)

Now we look at another type of enthalpy change.

■ 2.1 Measuring an enthalpy change of solution

When substances dissolve, the enthalpy change depends on the relative amounts of solute and solvent. Before you do the next experiment, we give a Worked Example to illustrate the calculations.

WORKED EXAMPLE

When 0.85 g of anhydrous lithium chloride, LiCl, was added to 36.0 g of water at 25.0°C in a polystyrene cup, the final temperature of the solution was 29.7°C. Calculate the enthalpy change of solution for one mole of lithium chloride.

Solution

1. In problems involving heat of solution, the amount of solvent is important so calculate the ratio: amount of LiCl/amount of H_2O. Then you can write the correct equation describing the process for one mole of the salt.

$$\text{amount of LiCl} = \frac{m}{M} = \frac{0.85\text{ g}}{42.4\text{ g mol}^{-1}} = 0.020\text{ mol}$$

$$\text{amount of H}_2\text{O} = \frac{m}{M} = \frac{36.0\text{ g}}{18.0\text{ g mol}^{-1}} = 2.00\text{ mol}$$

$$\therefore \frac{\text{amount of LiCl}}{\text{amount of H}_2\text{O}} = \frac{0.020}{2.00} = \frac{1}{100}$$

2. Write the equation:

$$\text{LiCl (s)} + 100\text{H}_2\text{O (l)} \rightarrow \text{LiCl (aq, 100H}_2\text{O)}$$

3. Calculate the enthalpy change for the amounts used in the experiment:

$$\begin{bmatrix}\text{enthalpy change, } \Delta H, \\ \text{on dissolving LiCl}\end{bmatrix} = \begin{bmatrix}\text{enthalpy change in restoring} \\ \text{solution to original temperature}\end{bmatrix}$$

$$\therefore \Delta H = mc_p\Delta T = \frac{36.0}{1000}\text{ kg} \times 4.18\text{ kJ kg}^{-1}\text{ K}^{-1} \times (-4.7\text{ K}) = -0.71\text{ kJ}$$

[Note that although the mass of the solution is greater than 36.0 g (36.85 g) its specific heat capacity is slightly **less** than 4.18 kJ kg^{-1} K^{-1}. The error arising from considering only the water in this type of calculation is therefore small.]

4. Scale up to the amounts shown in the equation, as in the last Worked Example:

$$\Delta H = -0.71\text{ kJ} \times \frac{1\text{ mol}}{0.020\text{ mol}} = -35\text{ kJ}$$

5. Write the complete thermochemical equation:

$$\text{LiCl (s)} + 100\text{H}_2\text{O (l)} \rightarrow \text{LiCl (aq, 100H}_2\text{O)}; \quad \Delta H_{\text{soln}} = -35 \text{ kJ mol}^{-1}$$

You can use this method of calculation in the next experiment, which your teacher may use for practical assessment.

EXPERIMENT 2   Determining an enthalpy change of solution

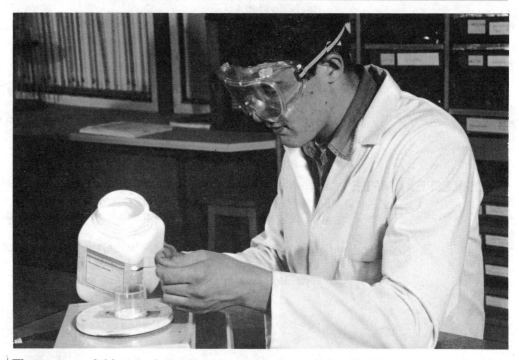

Aim   The purpose of this experiment is to determine the enthalpy change for the process

$$\text{NH}_4\text{Cl (s)} + 100\text{H}_2\text{O (l)} \rightarrow \text{NH}_4\text{Cl (aq, 100H}_2\text{O)}$$

Introduction   Because this is a planning experiment, we give fewer details and instructions than you have been used to. It is, of course, very similar to Experiment 1, but you need not plot a temperature/time graph because the maximum temperature change occurs rapidly and is, in any case, much smaller.

Requirements   Make a list of requirements including the masses and amounts needed; show the list to your teacher with your planned procedure.

Procedure   Work this out for yourself and keep an accurate record. Note that ammonium chloride is harmful if swallowed.

Results   1. Tabulate your results in an appropriate form.
2. Calculate the enthalpy change of solution for the thermochemical equation in the aim. (Your teacher has some specimen results.)

Question   Compare your result with the accepted value of $+16.4 \text{ kJ mol}^{-1}$. Suggest reasons for any difference.

Some enthalpy changes cannot be measured easily by direct experiment. However, you can often calculate them from the results of other experiments by using Hess' law, which we now consider.

CHAPTER **3** **HESS' LAW**

Hess' law (sometimes called Hess' law of constant heat summation) is a corollary to the law of conservation of energy. We use Hess' law to calculate enthalpy changes which cannot be measured directly.

OBJECTIVES
When you have finished this chapter you should be able to:
■ state **Hess' law**;
■ apply Hess' law in the calculation of enthalpy changes which cannot be determined experimentally.

 Study the section of your textbook which deals with Hess' law. Note down a statement of the law which you can remember and follow through an example of its application.

It is not possible to measure the enthalpy change for the reaction

$$C\,(s) + \tfrac{1}{2}O_2\,(g) \rightarrow CO\,(g)$$

directly in a calorimeter because it represents an incomplete combustion which cannot be controlled. However, it is possible to measure the enthalpy change for the complete combustion of both graphite and carbon monoxide, and we can **calculate** the heat of formation of carbon monoxide from these results. We illustrate Hess' law by showing this calculation, using an energy-level diagram, in a Worked Example.

WORKED EXAMPLE
Calculate the standard enthalpy change for the reaction

$$C\,(s) + \tfrac{1}{2}O_2\,(g) \rightarrow CO\,(g),$$

given the following information:

$$C\,(s) + O_2\,(g) \rightarrow CO_2\,(g); \quad \Delta H^\ominus = -394\ \text{kJ mol}^{-1}$$
$$CO\,(g) + \tfrac{1}{2}O_2\,(g) \rightarrow CO_2\,(g); \quad \Delta H^\ominus = -283\ \text{kJ mol}^{-1}$$

Solution
1. Draw an energy-level diagram to summarise the information given. Start by drawing a line to represent the enthalpy of 1 mol of graphite and 1 mol of oxygen at standard conditions.

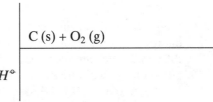

2. The combustion of 1 mol of graphite produces CO_2 and releases 394 kJ. Show this on the energy-level diagram (not necessarily to scale):

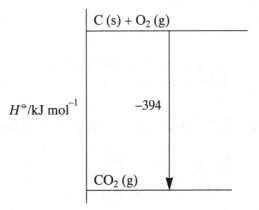

3. Now consider the combustion of CO, which gives the same product, 1 mol of CO_2. The energy released is 283 kJ mol^{-1}. Show this on the diagram:

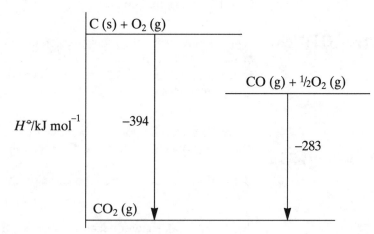

4. The gap between the two upper lines represents the heat of formation of carbon monoxide. Show this on the diagram:

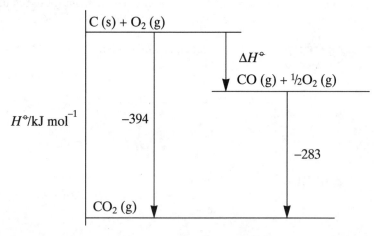

Don't worry about the 'extra' $\frac{1}{2}O_2$ in the two upper levels. Of course, the actual energy levels for C (s) + $\frac{1}{2}O_2$ (g) and for CO (g) would be a little lower, but the **difference** between them would be exactly the same.

5. So you have two routes to the formation of CO_2. One is represented by the heat of formation of CO_2 (g) and the other by the sum of two processes: the heat of formation of CO (g) plus the heat of combustion of CO (g). Hess' law states that the energy changes for the two routes are equal and you can see that this must be so from the energy-level diagram. Thus:

$$-394 \text{ kJ mol}^{-1} = \Delta H_f^\circ [\text{CO (g)}] + (-283 \text{ kJ mol}^{-1})$$

$$\therefore \Delta H_f^\circ [\text{CO (g)}] = (-394 + 283) \text{ kJ mol}^{-1} = \textbf{-111 kJ mol}^{-1}$$

An energy-level diagram clearly establishes the validity of Hess' law but, for solving problems, you may find it simpler to use an alternative method based on energy cycles.

■ 3.1 Use of energy cycles

An energy cycle simply shows two different routes between initial and final states, without reference to energy levels. We illustrate this by using the same example as before and showing two routes for the production of CO_2.

1. First represent the direct combination of elements:

2. Write the two-step process:

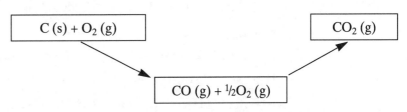

3. Hess' law tells us that the enthalpy change via one route ('route 1') must equal the enthalpy change via the two-step route ('route 2').

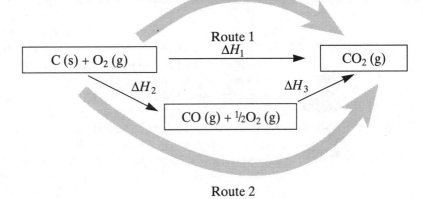

Route 2

$$\therefore \Delta H_1 = \Delta H_2 + \Delta H_3$$

4. Calculate the unknown by substituting the known values:

$$\Delta H_2 = \Delta H_1 - \Delta H_3$$

$$\therefore \Delta H_f^{\ominus}[CO\ (g)] = -394 \text{ kJ mol}^{-1} - (-283 \text{ kJ mol}^{-1}) = \textbf{−111 kJ mol}^{-1}$$

Both energy cycles and energy-level diagrams are very useful in solving problems. In the next exercise you use both methods: be careful to distinguish between the two. In an energy-level diagram, the arrows should be drawn vertically, and preferably to scale, to represent both direction and extent of enthalpy change. In an energy cycle, the arrows simply indicate a change from one state to another, and to avoid confusion we suggest you do not use vertical arrows in energy cycles.

EXERCISE 11

Answers on page 83

Calculate the standard enthalpy change for the reaction

$$2NO_2\ (g) \rightarrow N_2O_4\ (g)$$

given the thermochemical equations:

$$N_2\ (g) + 2O_2\ (g) \rightarrow 2NO_2\ (g); \quad \Delta H^{\ominus} = +33.2 \text{ kJ mol}^{-1}$$

$$N_2\ (g) + 2O_2\ (g) \rightarrow N_2O_4\ (g); \quad \Delta H^{\ominus} = +9.2 \text{ kJ mol}^{-1}$$

a by drawing an energy-level diagram,
b by drawing an energy cycle.

In the next exercise, you use and justify yet another way of applying Hess' law.

EXERCISE 12

Answers on page 83

Two of the possible methods of preparing a solution of ammonium chloride containing 1.00 mol of NH_4Cl in 200 mol of H_2O are summarised in the thermochemical equations below:

Method 1

NH_3 (g) + HCl (g) → NH_4Cl (s); ΔH°= –175.3 kJ mol^{-1}

NH_4Cl (s) + $200H_2O$ (l) → NH_4Cl (aq, $200H_2O$); ΔH°= +16.3 kJ mol^{-1}

Method 2

NH_3 (g) + $100H_2O$ (l) → NH_3 (aq, $100H_2O$); ΔH° = –35.6 kJ mol^{-1}

HCl (g) + $100H_2O$ (l) → HCl (aq, $100H_2O$); ΔH° = –73.2 kJ mol^{-1}

NH_3 (aq, $100H_2O$) + HCl (aq, $100H_2O$) → NH_4Cl (aq, $200H_2O$); ΔH° = –50.2 kJ mol^{-1}

a Add the equations in Method 1, and simplify the result.
b Add the equations in Method 2, and simplify the result.
c How does this illustrate Hess' law?
d Draw an energy-level diagram and an energy cycle.

We usually use the energy cycle method in the solutions we provide to exercises because it is the most general, but you may prefer to add equations as in Exercise 12. You should always be able to justify your method by means of an energy-level diagram.

In Experiment 3, you apply Hess' law to a reaction for which the enthalpy change cannot be measured directly – the hydration of magnesium sulphate, $MgSO_4$. The method and apparatus are very similar to those you used in Experiments 1 and 2.

In Appendix 3, we have included a similar experiment, the determination of the heat of hydration of copper(II) sulphate, $CuSO_4$. However, it is necessary to use a vacuum flask calorimeter, and both the practical work and the calculation are a little more difficult.

Ask your teacher which of these experiments you should do.

EXPERIMENT 3 Using Hess' law

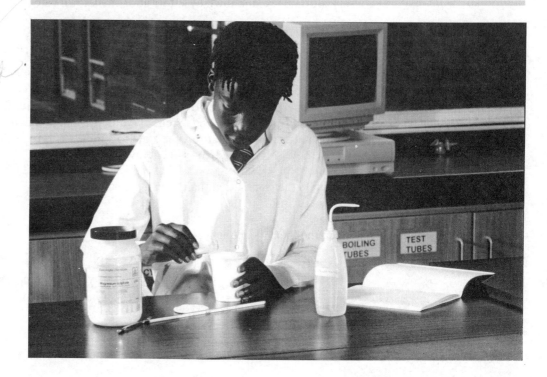

Aim   The purpose of this experiment is to determine the enthalpy change for the reaction

$$MgSO_4 \ (s) + 7H_2O \ (l) \rightarrow MgSO_4 \cdot 7H_2O \ (s)$$

Introduction   It is impossible to measure the enthalpy change for this reaction directly because the process cannot be controlled. However, you can calculate this enthalpy change by measuring the enthalpy change of solution for the two solids:

$$MgSO_4 \ (s) + 100H_2O \ (l) \rightarrow MgSO_4 \ (aq, 100H_2O)$$

$$MgSO_4 \cdot 7H_2O \ (s) + 93H_2O \ (l) \rightarrow MgSO_4 \ (aq, 100H_2O)$$

We suggest that you use 0.0250 mol of each salt, so we have calculated, from the equations, the required masses of each salt and water.

Requirements
- safety spectacles
- 2 weighing bottles
- spatula
- magnesium sulphate (anhydrous), $MgSO_4$
- access to balance
- 2 polystyrene cups and lids
- distilled water
- test pipette
- thermometer (0–50°C)
- magnesium sulphate-7-water, $MgSO_4 \cdot 7H_2O$

Procedure   **A. Heat of solution of $MgSO_4$ (s)**
1. Weigh 3.01 g of $MgSO_4$ to the nearest 0.01 g into a clean, dry weighing bottle. Record, in a copy of Results Table 2, the masses of weighing bottle empty and with contents, unless your balance has a reliable taring device.
2. Similarly, weigh 45.00 g of H_2O to the nearest 0.01 g into a polystyrene cup.
3. Put the thermometer through the hole in the lid and measure the temperature of the water. Record this in Results Table 2.
4. Carefully transfer the $MgSO_4$ into the water, stir gently with the thermometer, and record the maximum temperature.

B. Heat of solution of $MgSO_4 \cdot 7H_2O$
5. Weigh 6.16 g of $MgSO_4 \cdot 7H_2O$ to the nearest 0.01 g into a clean, dry weighing bottle.
6. Weigh 41.85 g of H_2O to the nearest 0.01 g into a polystyrene cup.
7. Measure and record the temperature change associated with dissolving the $MgSO_4 \cdot 7H_2O$

Results Table 2

	$MgSO_4$	$MgSO_4 \cdot 7H_2O$
Mass of weighing bottle		
Mass of weighing bottle + salt		
Mass of salt	3.01 g	6.16 g
Mass of polystyrene cup		
Mass of polystyrene cup + water		
Mass of water	45.00 g	41.85 g
Initial temperature		
Final temperature		

(Specimen results on page 84.)

Calculations

Specimen results on page 84

1. From the data in Results Table 2, calculate the enthalpy change of solution for one mole of $MgSO_4$. Assume $c_p = 4.18$ kJ kg^{-1} K^{-1}.
2. Similarly, calculate the enthalpy change of solution for one mole of $MgSO_4 \cdot 7H_2O$.
3. By means of an energy cycle, calculate the enthalpy change for the reaction:

$$MgSO_4 \text{ (s)} + 7H_2O \text{ (l)} \rightarrow MgSO_4 \cdot 7H_2O \text{ (s)}$$

Questions

Answers on page 85

1. Plot the results on an energy-level diagram.
2. Why is it not necessary to plot a temperature/time graph as you did in Experiment 1?
3. Compare your result with the accepted value of -104 kJ mol^{-1}. Suggest reasons for any difference.

Now we look at another application of Hess' law.

■ 3.2 Calculating enthalpy of formation from enthalpy of combustion

As you will see later, it is particularly useful to list enthalpy changes of formation for compounds. However, most compounds cannot be formed directly from the elements, so it is impossible to measure these enthalpy changes in a calorimeter.

One of the most useful applications of Hess' law is in calculating heat of formation from heats of combustion, which can be measured directly.

OBJECTIVE

When you have finished this section you should be able to:
■ calculate ΔH_f° of a compound from values of ΔH_c° for the compound and for its constituent elements.

We illustrate the calculation by a Worked Example, but to help you follow it you should read the section in your textbook on this topic, paying particular attention to the explanation of the calculation procedure.

WORKED EXAMPLE

Calculate the standard enthalpy of formation of ethane, C_2H_6, given:

$$C \text{ (s)} + O_2 \text{ (g)} \rightarrow CO_2 \text{ (g)}; \quad \Delta H^\circ = -394 \text{ kJ mol}^{-1}.$$

$$H_2 \text{ (g)} + \tfrac{1}{2}O_2 \text{ (g)} \rightarrow H_2O \text{ (l)}; \quad \Delta H^\circ = -286 \text{ kJ mol}^{-1}.$$

$$C_2H_6 \text{ (g)} + 3\tfrac{1}{2}O_2 \text{ (g)} \rightarrow 2CO_2 \text{ (g)} + 3H_2O \text{ (l)}; \quad \Delta H^\circ = -1560 \text{ kJ mol}^{-1}.$$

Solution

1. Starting with the reaction for which you want to calculate ΔH_f°, begin to construct an energy cycle:

2. Put in the combustion reactions:

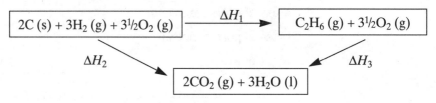

Note that the inclusion of $3\tfrac{1}{2}O_2$ (g), which is necessary for the combustion, makes no difference to ΔH_1 (see Exercise 6).

3. Use Hess' law to equate the enthalpy changes.

$$\Delta H_2 = \Delta H_1 + \Delta H_3$$

or

$$\Delta H_1 = \Delta H_2 - \Delta H_3$$

4. Substitute numerical values for ΔH_2 and ΔH_3.

$$\Delta H_2 = 2\Delta H_c^\ominus \, [\text{C (s)}] + 3\Delta H_c^\ominus \, [\text{H}_2 \text{ (g)}]$$

$$= 2(-394 \text{ kJ mol}^{-1}) + 3(-286 \text{ kJ mol}^{-1})$$

$$= (-788 - 858 \text{ kJ mol}^{-1}) = -1646 \text{ kJ mol}^{-1}$$

$$\Delta H_3 = \Delta H_c^\ominus \, [\text{C}_2\text{H}_6 \text{ (g)}] = -1560 \text{ kJ mol}^{-1}$$

$$\therefore \Delta H_1 = \Delta H_2 - \Delta H_3$$

$$= -1646 \text{ kJ mol}^{-1} - (-1560 \text{ kJ mol}^{-1}) = \mathbf{-86 \text{ kJ mol}^{-1}}$$

Now try the next two exercises to test your understanding of this application of Hess' law.

EXERCISE 13
Answer on page 85

Calculate the standard enthalpy change of formation of carbon disulphide, CS_2, given that

$$\Delta H_f^\ominus [\text{CO}_2 \text{ (g)}] = -393.5 \text{ kJ mol}^{-1},$$

$$\Delta H_f^\ominus [\text{SO}_2 \text{ (g)}] = -296.9 \text{ kJ mol}^{-1},$$

$$\Delta H_c^\ominus [\text{CS}_2 \text{ (l)}] = -1075.2 \text{ kJ mol}^{-1}.$$

EXERCISE 14
Answers on page 86

Calculate the standard enthalpy change of formation of the following compounds:
a ethane, C_2H_6,
b ethanol, C_2H_5OH,
c methylamine, CH_3NH_2,
   Hint: For part **c** assume that when CH_3NH_2 burns, nitrogen is released as N_2 (g).

Having shown you how enthalpy changes of formation can be calculated, we now consider what use can be made of the values.

■ 3.3 Uses of standard enthalpy changes of formation

In your data book you will find lists of enthalpy changes of formation for both organic and inorganic compounds. Many of the values have been calculated from experimental results in ways similar to those we have described; now you learn how to use them.

OBJECTIVE

When you have finished this section you should be able to:
■ use **standard enthalpy changes of formation** to calculate the **standard enthalpy change for a reaction**.

Standard enthalpy changes of formation can be used to calculate the enthalpy changes in a reaction. The fact that we can predict the enthalpy change for any reaction is vitally important, for instance, to chemical engineers when planning a chemical plant. They need to know how much heat will be generated or absorbed during the course of a particular reaction and make adequate provision for extremes of temperature in their designs.

Read the section of your textbook which describes the calculation paying particular attention to the derivation of the expression:

$$\Delta H^{\ominus}_{\text{reaction}} = \Sigma \Delta H^{\ominus}_{\text{f}} (\text{products}) - \Sigma \Delta H^{\ominus}_{\text{f}} (\text{reactants}),$$

where the symbol Σ means 'the sum of'.

You should now be able to work through the following Revealing Exercise, which is in the form of a series of short questions and answers. (See the Introduction to ILPAC.)

EXERCISE

Revealing

Consider the energy cycle:

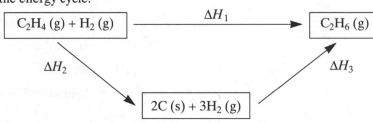

Q1 Identify two routes for the conversion of C_2H_4 and H_2 to C_2H_6.

A1 Route 1. Direct combination.
   Route 2. i) Decomposition of C_2H_4 to the elements, followed by
   ii) formation of C_2H_6 from the elements.

Q2 Write down the enthalpy changes for each route.

A2 Route 1. ΔH_1
   Route 2. $\Delta H_2 + \Delta H_3$

Q3 Apply Hess' law to obtain an expression for ΔH_1 in terms of ΔH_2 and ΔH_3.

A3 $\Delta H_1 = \Delta H_2 + \Delta H_3$

Q4 How would you obtain values for ΔH_2 and ΔH_3?

A4 Look up $\Delta H^{\ominus}_{\text{f}}[C_2H_4 \text{ (g)}]$ and $\Delta H^{\ominus}_{\text{f}}[C_2H_6 \text{ (g)}]$. $\Delta H_2 = -\Delta H^{\ominus}_{\text{f}}[C_2H_4 \text{ (g)}]$.

Q5 Why is it not necessary to look up $\Delta H^{\ominus}_{\text{f}}[H_2 \text{ (g)}]$?

A5 $\Delta H^{\ominus}_{\text{f}}$ for elements in their standard states is, by definition, zero – since it refers to a change between identical states, i.e. no change at all!

Q6 Rewrite the expression in **A3**, using symbols for heats of formation.

A6 $\Delta H_1 = \Delta H^{\ominus}_{\text{f}}[C_2H_6 \text{ (g)}] - \Delta H^{\ominus}_{\text{f}}[C_2H_4 \text{ (g)}]$

Q7 Show that this is a particular case of the general expression

$$\Delta H_{\text{r}} = \Sigma \Delta H^{\ominus}_{\text{f}}[\text{products}] - \Sigma \Delta H^{\ominus}_{\text{f}}[\text{reactants}]$$

A7 $\Sigma\Delta H_f^\ominus[\text{products}]$ = $\Delta H_f^\ominus[\text{C}_2\text{H}_6 \text{ (g)}]$

$\Sigma\Delta H_f^\ominus[\text{reactants}]$ = $\Delta H_f^\ominus[\text{C}_2\text{H}_4 \text{ (g)}]$ + $\Delta H_f^\ominus[\text{H}_2 \text{ (g)}]$

$= \Delta H_f^\ominus[\text{C}_2\text{H}_4 \text{ (g)}]$ + 0 (see **A5**)

$= \Delta H_f^\ominus[\text{C}_2\text{H}_4 \text{ (g)}]$

$\Delta H_1 = \Sigma\Delta H_f^\ominus[\text{products}] - \Sigma\Delta H_f^\ominus [\text{reactants}]$

$= \Delta H_f^\ominus[\text{C}_2\text{H}_6 \text{ (g)}] - \Delta H_f^\ominus[\text{C}_2\text{H}_4 \text{ (g)}]$

Q8 Use your data book to calculate a value for ΔH_1.

A8 $\Delta H_1 = \Delta H_f^\ominus[\text{C}_2\text{H}_6 \text{ (g)}] - \Delta H_f^\ominus[\text{C}_2\text{H}_4 \text{ (g)}]$
$= -84.6 \text{ kJ mol}^{-1} - (+52.3 \text{ kJ mol}^{-1}) = \mathbf{-136.9 \text{ kJ mol}^{-1}}$

You can apply the same procedure to any reaction. However, once you have understood the derivation of the expression

$$3\Delta H_r^\ominus = \Sigma\Delta H_f^\ominus[\text{products}] - \Sigma\Delta H_f^\ominus[\text{reactants}]$$

you can use it to solve problems without drawing an energy cycle, as we show in a Worked Example.

WORKED EXAMPLE Calculate the standard enthalpy change for the reaction

$$2\text{H}_2\text{S (g)} + \text{SO}_2 \text{ (g)} \rightarrow 3\text{S (s)} + 2\text{H}_2\text{O (l)}$$

using only standard enthalpy of formation data.

Compound	$\Delta H_f^\ominus/\text{kJ mol}^{-1}$
$\text{H}_2\text{S (g)}$	−20.6
$\text{SO}_2 \text{ (g)}$	−296.9
$\text{H}_2\text{O (l)}$	−285.9

Solution 1. Write an equation, leaving room to put the value of $\Delta H_f^\ominus$ under each formula.

$$2\text{H}_2\text{S (g)} + \text{SO}_2 \text{ (g)} \rightarrow 3\text{S (s)} + 2\text{H}_2\text{O (l)}$$

2. Calculate the standard enthalpy change of formation for the amount specified in the equation for each substance. In this equation, 2 mol of $\text{H}_2\text{O (l)}$ are produced.

$$2 \Delta H_f^\ominus [\text{H}_2\text{O (l)}] = -571.8 \text{ kJ mol}^{-1}$$

Similarly, for $\text{H}_2\text{S (g)}$, $2 \Delta H_f^\ominus [\text{H}_2\text{S (g)}] = -41.2 \text{ kJ mol}^{-1}$ and for $\text{SO}_2 \text{ (g)}$, $\Delta H_f^\ominus [\text{SO}_2 \text{ (g)}] = -296.9 \text{ kJ mol}^{-1}$. Because $\Delta H_f^\ominus$ for all elements in their standard states is zero, no value appears for sulphur.

3. Put these values under the compounds to which they refer.

$$2\text{H}_2\text{S (g)} + \text{SO}_2 \text{ (g)} \rightarrow 3\text{S (s)} + 2\text{H}_2\text{O (l)}$$

$\Delta H_f^\ominus/\text{kJ mol}^{-1}$ −41.2   −296.9   0   −571.8

4. Add the values for the products.

$$\Sigma\Delta H_f^\ominus [\text{products}] = (0 - 571.8) \text{ kJ mol}^{-1} = -571.8 \text{ kJ mol}^{-1}$$

Add the values for the reactants.

$$\Sigma\Delta H_f^\ominus[\text{reactants}] = (-41.2 - 296.9) \text{ kJ mol}^{-1} = -338.1 \text{ kJ mol}^{-1}$$

5. Subtract:

$$\Delta H_r = \Sigma \Delta H_f^\ominus [\text{products}] - \Sigma \Delta H_f^\ominus [\text{reactants}]$$

$$= [-571.8 - (-338.1)] \text{ kJ mol}^{-1} = \mathbf{-233.7 \text{ kJ mol}^{-1}}$$

Now try some examples for yourself. Be very careful about positive and negative signs.

EXERCISE 15
Answers on page 86

Calculate the standard enthalpy changes for the following reactions. Obtain values of $\Delta H_f^\ominus$ from your data book.

a CH_3OH (l) + $1\frac{1}{2}O_2$ (g) $\rightarrow$ CO_2 (g) + $2H_2O$ (l)

b $2CO$ (g) + O_2 (g) $\rightarrow$ $2CO_2$ (g)

c $ZnCO_3$ (s) $\rightarrow$ ZnO (s) + CO_2 (g)

d $2Al$ (s) + Fe_2O_3 (s) $\rightarrow$ $2Fe$ (s) + Al_2O_3 (s)

EXERCISE 16
Answer on page 87

The standard enthalpies of formation ($\Delta H_f^\ominus$) at 298 K for a number of compounds are, in kJ mol^{-1}:

$$CH_4 \text{ (g)} - 75; \ H_2O \text{ (g)} - 242; \ CO \text{ (g)} - 110$$

Calculate the enthalpy change for the reaction:

$$CH_4 \text{ (g)} + H_2O \text{ (g)} \rightarrow CO \text{ (g)} + 3H_2 \text{ (g)}$$

 Another important use of enthalpy changes of formation is the prediction of the relative stabilities of compounds. However, it is important to clarify what we mean by the word 'stability', which we do in the next chapter.

CHAPTER 4

ENERGETIC AND KINETIC STABILITY

Figure 9

We can discuss the stability of the man at the top of the ladder (Fig. 9) in two different ways. He is unstable in that if he misses his footing or is pushed, he would fall to the ground. He is liable to fall from a position of high potential energy to one of lower potential energy. We can therefore say that his position is one of energetic instability.

However, if he stands carefully, he can stay at the top of the ladder indefinitely. The rate at which he actually falls to the ground is then zero, even though we might expect him to fall by consideration of energy levels. The word 'kinetic' refers to the rate of a process; thus, we can say that the man is kinetically stable.

OBJECTIVES

When you have finished this chapter you should be able to:
- distinguish between **kinetic** and **energetic (thermodynamic) stability**;
- describe compounds as stable or unstable with respect to specified substances, using the enthalpy change of reaction.

Read the appropriate section in your textbook, looking for other examples of kinetic and energetic stability to clarify the concepts. (You may find the term **thermodynamic stability** used for energetic stability.) Look also for the way in which stability may be inferred from values of enthalpy change so that you can do the following exercises.

EXERCISE 17

Answers on page 87

a Would you expect a compound with a negative value of $\Delta H_f^{\ominus}$ to be stable or unstable? Explain your answer.

b Draw an energy-level diagram showing the enthalpy change of formation of H_2O_2 (l).

c Calculate the enthalpy change for the reaction:

$$H_2O_2 \text{ (l)} \rightarrow H_2O \text{ (l)} + \tfrac{1}{2}O_2 \text{ (g)}$$

Show this on the same energy-level diagram.

d Comment on the energetic stability of H_2O_2 (l).

EXERCISE 18

Answer on page 87

Comment on the thermodynamic stability of NO (g). Base your answer on the two equations:

$$\tfrac{1}{2}N_2 \text{ (g)} + \tfrac{1}{2}O_2 \text{ (g)} \rightarrow NO \text{ (g)}; \quad \Delta H^{\ominus} = +90 \text{ kJ mol}^{-1}$$

$$NO \text{ (g)} + \tfrac{1}{2}O_2 \text{ (g)} \rightarrow NO_2 \text{ (g)}; \quad \Delta H^{\ominus} = -74 \text{ kJ mol}^{-1}$$

EXERCISE 19

Answers on page 87

Comment on the stability of ethyne, C_2H_2, relative to the elements and relative to benzene, C_6H_6.

$$3C_2H_2 \text{ (g)} \xrightarrow{\text{catalyst}} C_6H_6 \text{ (l)}$$

EXERCISE 20

Answers on page 88

The standard enthalpy of formation at 298 K of carbon dioxide, CO_2, is -394 kJ mol^{-1} whilst that of carbon monoxide, CO, is -110 kJ mol^{-1}.

a State precisely what is meant by standard enthalpy of formation.

b i) Calculate the enthalpy change for the reaction:

$$CO_2 \text{ (g)} \rightarrow CO \text{ (g)} + \tfrac{1}{2}O_2 \text{ (g)}$$

ii) Are these oxides of carbon thermodynamically stable or unstable with respect to carbon and oxygen? Explain.

The exercises you have just done suggest that you can predict whether a particular reaction can occur or not simply by calculating ΔH°. Although this is a useful idea, you have to be careful in applying it, as we now show.

■ 4.1 Using ΔH° values to predict the direction of change

Just as we would expect the man to fall off the ladder if he were given a push, we might expect any reaction which has a negative value for its enthalpy change to proceed spontaneously. It may not happen, of course, if the system is kinetically stable. Such a system is

$$H_2 \text{ (g)} + \tfrac{1}{2}O_2 \text{ (g)} \rightarrow H_2O \text{ (l)}; \Delta H^\circ = -286 \text{ kJ mol}^{-1}$$

Hydrogen and oxygen can stay mixed for years with no sign of reaction. But in the presence of a spark (similar to a 'push' causing the man to fall from the ladder) the reaction proceeds explosively.

However, there are reactions with positive values of ΔH° which also proceed spontaneously; e.g.

$$6SOCl_2 \text{ (l)} + FeCl_3 \cdot 6H_2O \text{ (s)} \rightarrow FeCl_3 \text{ (s)} + 6SO_2 \text{ (g)} + 12HCl \text{ (g)}; \quad \Delta H^\circ = +1271 \text{ kJ mol}^{-1}$$

Your teacher may be able to demonstrate this for you.

Conversely, there are some reactions with negative values of ΔH° which do **not** proceed spontaneously, even with a 'push' or a catalyst to increase the rate. One example is:

$$N_2 \text{ (g)} + 2\tfrac{1}{2}O_2 \text{ (g)} \rightarrow N_2O_5 \text{ (s)}; \quad \Delta H^\circ = -43.1 \text{ kJ mol}^{-1}$$

And, of course, you know a number of reactions which can go in either direction. These reversible reactions may have positive or negative values of ΔH°, depending on the way the equation is written.

$$N_2 \text{ (g)} + 3H_2 \text{ (g)} \rightleftharpoons 2NH_3 \text{ (g)}; \quad \Delta H^\circ = -92.0 \text{ kJ mol}^{-1}$$

$$2NH_3 \text{ (g)} \rightleftharpoons N_2 \text{ (g)} + 3H_2 \text{ (g)}; \quad \Delta H^\circ = +92.0 \text{ kJ mol}^{-1}$$

Obviously, our 'ladder' analogy, like most analogies, must not be pressed too far – we **never** expect to see a man fall **up** a ladder, nor to remain suspended at the top if he is pushed off!

So, it is clear that enthalpy changes alone do not govern the direction in which a reaction can proceed. The quantity we should use is the standard free energy change, ΔG°, and you may learn more about this later in the course. It is ΔG° and not ΔH° which is negative for a reaction which goes to completion.

Even if the study of ΔG° is excluded from your A-level syllabus, we think it may be well worth your while to look at an introduction to the topic, particularly if you are thinking of studying chemistry beyond A-level. Discuss with your teacher how far you should go.

Fortunately, however, $\Delta G^{\ominus}$ is closely related to $\Delta H^{\ominus}$ and for most reactions (at 298 K) has similar values. Check this in your data book by looking up values of $\Delta G_f^{\ominus}$ and $\Delta H_f^{\ominus}$; they are usually tabulated in adjacent columns.

Provided $\Delta G_f^{\ominus}$ values are known, you can calculate $\Delta G^{\ominus}$ for a reaction just as you calculated $\Delta H^{\ominus}$. Use the relationship:

$$\Delta G^{\ominus} = \Sigma \Delta G_f^{\ominus} [\text{products}] - \Sigma \Delta G_f^{\ominus} [\text{reactants}]$$

EXERCISE 21

Answers on page 88

Calculate $\Delta G^{\ominus}$ for the following reactions and compare your answers with the values of $\Delta H^{\ominus}$ calculated in Exercise 15. Comment on any difference.

a $CH_3OH\ (l) + 1\frac{1}{2}O_2\ (g) \rightarrow CO_2\ (g) + 2H_2O\ (l)$

b $2CO\ (g) + O_2\ (g) \rightarrow 2CO_2\ (g)$

c $ZnCO_3\ (s) \rightarrow ZnO\ (s) + CO_2\ (g)$

d $2Al\ (s) + Fe_2O_3\ (s) \rightarrow 2Fe\ (s) + Al_2O_3\ (s)$

The last exercise illustrates the fact that $\Delta H^{\ominus}$ is usually a good guide for predicting the relative stabilities of substances and the direction of change. You will often use $\Delta H^{\ominus}$ for this purpose, but you should remember that it is better to use $\Delta G^{\ominus}$, if values are available (frequently they are not!).

(Free energy is often called 'Gibbs energy' or 'Gibbs free energy' after the famous American thermodynamicist, J. Willard Gibbs, who first introduced the term – hence the use of the letter G.)

■ Part A test

To find out how well you have learned the material in Part A, try the test which follows. Read the notes below before starting.

1. You should spend about 1 hour on this test.
2. Hand your answers to your teacher for marking.

For each of the questions 1 to 3, **one** or **more** of the responses given is/are correct. Decide which of the responses is/are correct and then choose

A if **1, 2** and **3** are correct,
B if **1** and **2** only are correct,
C if **2** and **3** only are correct,
D if **1** only is correct,
E if **3** only is correct.

Directions summarised				
A	B	C	D	E
1, 2, 3	**1, 2**	**2, 3**	**1**	**3**
correct	only	only	only	only

1. The standard enthalpy of formation of hydrogen peroxide is represented by the following equation:

$$H_2 \text{ (g)} + O_2 \text{ (g)} \rightarrow H_2O_2 \text{ (l)}; \quad \Delta H_f^{\ominus} = -188 \text{ kJ mol}^{-1}$$

This suggests that hydrogen peroxide
1 will not decompose readily into water and oxygen,
2 releases heat energy when prepared from its elements,
3 is energetically stable with respect to its elements. (1)

2. For the following series of changes

$$CH_4 \text{ (g)} \rightarrow CH_3 \text{ (g)} + H \text{ (g)} \quad \Delta H_1$$
$$CH_3 \text{ (g)} \rightarrow CH_2 \text{ (g)} + H \text{ (g)} \quad \Delta H_2$$
$$CH_2 \text{ (g)} \rightarrow CH \text{ (g)} + H \text{ (g)} \quad \Delta H_3$$
$$CH \text{ (g)} \rightarrow C \text{ (g)} + H \text{ (g)} \quad \Delta H_4$$

correct statements include:
1 The mean C—H bond enthalpy is $\frac{1}{4}(\Delta H_1 + \Delta H_2 + \Delta H_3 + \Delta H_4)$,
2 $\Delta H_1, \Delta H_2, \Delta H_3$ and ΔH_4 are all equal,
3 $-(\Delta H_1 + \Delta H_2 + \Delta H_3 + \Delta H_4)$ is the standard enthalpy of formation of methane. (1)

In Question 3, if you have not studied ΔG, assume that $\Delta G^{\ominus} \approx \Delta H^{\ominus}$.

3. At 2000 K, the standard free energy changes, per mole of O_2, for the following reactions are

Table 1

Equation	$\Delta G^{\ominus}$/kJ
$2C + O_2 \rightarrow 2CO$	−520
$2Mg + O_2 \rightarrow 2MgO$	−490
$\frac{4}{3}Al + O_2 \rightarrow \frac{2}{3}Al_2O_3$	−700

This shows that at 2000 K
1 carbon should reduce magnesium oxide
2 carbon should reduce aluminium oxide
3 magnesium should reduce aluminium oxide   (1)

Questions 4 to 6 are either questions or incomplete statements followed by five suggested answers. Select the best answer in each case.

4. The following are standard enthalpies of formation in kJ mol^{-1}:

   CO_2 (g): -394 H_2O (g): -242 CO (g): -110

   What is the standard enthalpy change, in kJ mol^{-1}, for the reaction

   CO (g) + H_2O (g) $\rightarrow$ CO_2 (g) + H_2 (g)?

   A -42 B $+42$ C -262 D $+262$ E -526 (1)

5. Consider the following thermochemical equations:

   H_2 (g) + $\frac{1}{2}O_2$ (g) $\rightarrow$ H_2O (l); $\Delta H^\circ = -286$ kJ mol^{-1}

   H_2O (l) $\rightarrow$ H_2O (g); $\Delta H^\circ = +44$ kJ mol^{-1}

   The enthalpy change, in kJ mol^{-1}, for the reaction

   $2H_2$ (g) + O_2 (g) $\rightarrow$ $2H_2O$ (g) is

   A -484
   B -242
   C $+242$
   D $+484$
   E -330 (1)

6.
	CS_2 (l)	NOCl (g)	CCl_4 (l)	SO_2 (g)
ΔH_f° (298)/kJ mol^{-1}	88	53	-139	-296

   From the data above, the value of ΔH° (298) in kJ mol^{-1}, for the reaction

   CS_2 (l) + 4NOCl (g) $\rightarrow$ CCl_4 (l) + $2SO_2$ (g) + $2N_2$ (g) is

   A -1031,
   B -731,
   C -431,
   D $+431$,
   E $+1031$.   (1)

7. **a** Write a thermochemical equation to summarise the following statement.
       'When a mole of anhydrous copper(II) chloride (melting point 771 K) is formed from its elements at a temperature of 800 K, and under constant pressure conditions, 210 kJ of heat is evolved.'   (3)
   b Draw an energy-level diagram (not to scale) to represent the information given above.   (2)
   c i) Define standard enthalpy of formation.   (2)
       ii) What value is assigned to the standard enthalpy of formation of an element in its standard state?   (1)
   d i) Why can the enthalpies of formation of compounds not always be determined by direct experiment?   (2)
       ii) State, and briefly explain, the law which allows such enthalpies of formation to be calculated.   (3)

8. Chemical companies manufacture containers filled with liquid butane for use by campers. The enthalpy change of combustion of butane is –3000 kJ mol⁻¹.

   a Write an equation for the complete combustion of butane. (1)

   A camper estimates that the liquid butane left in a container would give 1.2 dm³ of butane gas (measured at ordinary temperature and pressure).

   b Calculate the mass of water at 20°C that could be brought to the boiling point by burning this butane: use the following information.

   Assume that 80% of the heat from the butane is absorbed by the water, the specific heat capacity of water is 4.2 J g⁻¹ K⁻¹, and 1 mol of a gas occupies 24 dm³ at ordinary temperatures and pressures. (3)

   c Suggest how the camper might have estimated how much butane was left in the container. (1)

   d When burnt in a limited supply of air, butane forms carbon and steam.

   i) Construct a balanced equation for this reaction.
   The enthalpy change of this reaction is –1400 kJ mol⁻¹.

   ii) Explain why the enthalpy changes of these two combustion reactions are different.

   iii) What additional quantitative information can be calculated from this difference? (3)

9. **a** Calculate the standard enthalpy of formation of ethanoic acid, CH_3CO_2H (l), from the following data:
   $\Delta H_c^\ominus$ [graphite] = –394 kJ mol⁻¹
   $\Delta H_c^\ominus$ [H_2 (g)] = –286 kJ mol⁻¹
   $\Delta H_c^\ominus$ [CH_3CO_2H (l)] = –873.2 kJ mol⁻¹ (4)

   b What can you deduce about the stability of ethanoic acid? (2)

   c What further information would you need to make a more reliable statement about the stability of ethanoic acid? (2)

10. **a** Use the data in Table 2 to determine $\Delta H^\ominus$ and $\Delta G^\ominus$ for the following reactions:

    N_2O_5 (s) → $2NO_2$ (g) + $\frac{1}{2}O_2$ (g)

    N_2O_5 (s) → N_2O_4 (g) + $\frac{1}{2}O_2$ (g)

Table 2

Compound	$\Delta H_f^\ominus$/kJ mol⁻¹	$\Delta G_f^\ominus$/kJ mol⁻¹
N_2O_5 (s)	–43.1	+113.8
NO_2 (g)	+33.2	+51.3
N_2O_4 (g)	+9.2	+97.8

(6)

   b Would you expect N_2O_5 (s) to be stable? (3)

(Total: 44 marks)

In this part we consider in more detail the energetics of bond formation. First we consider covalent molecules and introduce the idea of an average bond energy; then we consider the energetics of ionic bond formation.

BOND ENERGY TERM (BOND ENTHALPY TERM)

The energy required to break a particular bond depends not only on the nature of the two bonded atoms but also on the environment of those atoms. For instance, not all the C—H bonds in ethanol, C_2H_5OH, are equally strong because the oxygen atom has more influence on those near it than on those further away.

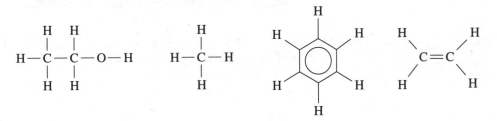

Similarly, C—H bonds in methane, CH_4, are not quite the same as those in benzene, C_6H_6, or ethene, C_2H_4. Fortunately, however, the differences are small enough for the concept of **average** bond energy (bond energy term) to be very useful.

OBJECTIVES

When you have finished this chapter you should be able to:
- state what is meant by **bond energy term**;
- distinguish between **bond dissociation energy** and bond energy term.

Read about bond energy term (sometimes just called **bond energy** or **average bond energy**) in your textbook, paying particular attention to the difference between bond energy term and **bond dissociation energy**. Some books more correctly use 'enthalpy' instead of 'energy' in these terms. This will help you to do the next two exercises.

EXERCISE 22

Answers on page 88

Table 3

Table 3 gives enthalpy changes for four successive dissociation reactions:

Reaction	$\Delta H^\circ/\text{kJ mol}^{-1}$
$CH_4\ (g) \rightarrow CH_3\ (g) + H\ (g)$	+435
$CH_3\ (g) \rightarrow CH_2\ (g) + H\ (g)$	+444
$CH_2\ (g) \rightarrow CH\ (g) + H\ (g)$	+440
$CH\ (g) \rightarrow C\ (g) + H\ (g)$	+343

a Calculate the enthalpy change for the reaction

$$CH_4 (g) \rightarrow C (g) + 4H (g)$$

b Calculate the average bond energy of a C—H bond in methane.
c What name do we give each of the enthalpy changes in Table 3?
d Suggest a reason why each is different.

EXERCISE 23
Answers on page 89

a Explain the difference between 'bond energy term' and 'bond dissociation energy'.
b Name a molecule for which the bond dissociation energy is the same as the bond energy term.

We cannot always obtain bond energy terms by the method you have just used because bond dissociation energies are often not known. In the next section we look at another method of calculation.

■ 5.1 Calculating bond energy terms

Once again we can use an energy cycle and Hess' law to determine an enthalpy change which cannot be measured directly. We illustrate this method by a Worked Example.

OBJECTIVE

When you have finished this section you should be able to:
■ calculate the bond energy term for a molecule using standard heat of formation data and **standard enthalpy of atomisation** data.

The standard enthalpy change of atomisation of an element is the enthalpy change in the production of one mole of gaseous atoms from the element in its standard state. For example, it refers to processes such as

$$Na (s) \rightarrow Na (g) \quad and \quad \tfrac{1}{2}Cl_2 (g) \rightarrow Cl (g)$$

We deal with the atomisation of compounds later.

WORKED EXAMPLE

Calculate the C—H bond energy term in methane.

Solution

1. Write the equation for the complete dissociation of methane.

$$CH_4 (g) \rightarrow C (g) + 4H (g)$$

2. Construct an energy cycle by including the elements in their standard states.

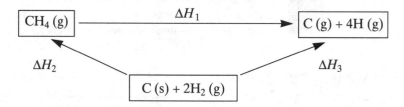

Here ΔH_2 is the standard enthalpy change of formation of methane, $\Delta H_f^{\ominus} [CH_4 (g)]$; and ΔH_3 is the standard enthalpy change of atomisation of carbon plus four times the standard enthalpy change of atomisation of hydrogen; i.e.

$$\Delta H_3 = \Delta H_{at}^{\ominus} [C (g)] + 4 \, \Delta H_{at}^{\ominus} [H (g)].$$

3. Look up these values in your data book:

$$\Delta H_f^{\ominus} [CH_4 \, (g)] = -74.8 \text{ kJ mol}^{-1}$$

$$\Delta H_{at}^{\ominus} [C \, (g)] = +715.0 \text{ kJ mol}^{-1}$$

$$4 \, \Delta H_{at}^{\ominus} [H \, (g)] = 4(+218.0 \text{ kJ mol}^{-1}) = 872.0 \text{ kJ mol}^{-1}$$

Note that the value listed here is 'per mole of H atoms formed', not 'per mole of H_2 molecules atomised'.

4. Apply Hess' law: $\Delta H_2 + \Delta H_1 = \Delta H_3$.

5. Substitute the appropriate values and solve for ΔH_1:

$$\Delta H_1 = \Delta H_3 - \Delta H_2$$
$$= (715.0 + 872.0 - (-74.8)) \text{ kJ mol}^{-1} = 1661.8 \text{ kJ mol}^{-1}$$

6. This is the energy required to break four bonds. We want to know the average value for one bond.

$$\therefore \overline{E}(C-H) = \frac{1661.8}{4} \text{ kJ mol}^{-1} = \textbf{415 kJ mol}^{-1}$$

Now try two similar problems.

EXERCISE 24
Answers on page 89

Determine the enthalpy change for the process:

$$H_2S \, (g) \rightarrow 2H \, (g) + S \, (g)$$

and so calculate the bond energy term, $\overline{E}(H-S)$.

EXERCISE 25
Answers on page 89

Calculate $\overline{E}(N-H)$, given the following data:
$\frac{1}{2}N_2 \, (g) + \frac{3}{2}H_2 \, (g) \rightarrow NH_3 \, (g); \quad \Delta H^{\ominus} = -46 \text{ kJ mol}^{-1}$
$\frac{1}{2}H_2 \, (g) \rightarrow H \, (g); \quad \Delta H^{\ominus} = +218 \text{ kJ mol}^{-1}$
$\frac{1}{2}N_2 \, (g) \rightarrow N \, (g); \quad \Delta H^{\ominus} = +473 \text{ kJ mol}^{-1}$

Notice that in all these examples and exercises, reactants and products are in the **gaseous** state. If the substance we are decomposing exists as a liquid in its standard state, it must first be vaporised, and this requires energy.

$$CCl_4 \, (l) \rightarrow CCl_4 \, (g); \quad \Delta H_{vap}^{\ominus} [CCl_4 \, (l)] = 30.5 \text{ kJ mol}^{-1}$$

Apply this idea in the next exercise.

EXERCISE 26
Answers on page 89

Calculate the enthalpy change for the process

$$CCl_4 \, (g) \rightarrow C \, (g) + 4Cl \, (g)$$

and calculate the bond energy term, $\overline{E}(C-Cl)$.

So far you have averaged energies for **similar** bonds within **identical** molecules. Now you investigate the validity of assuming that bond energy terms can be applied to similar bonds in **different** molecules. Start by working out, in the next exercise, what bonds are broken and formed in the combustion of some similar alcohols.

OBJECTIVES   When you have finished this section you should be able to:
- describe briefly how the **enthalpies of combustion** of a series of alcohols can be measured;
- interpret enthalpy of combustion data for a series of alcohols in terms of bonds broken and bonds formed.

EXERCISE 27

Answers on page 90

This question concerns the combustion of a number of alcohols. The structural formulae of some of these alcohols and of the other substances involved are:

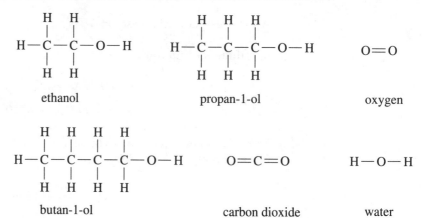

ethanol   propan-1-ol   oxygen

butan-1-ol   carbon dioxide   water

Two equations for combustion are:

$$C_2H_5OH \text{ (l)} + 3O_2 \text{ (g)} \rightarrow 2CO_2 \text{ (g)} + 3H_2O \text{ (l)}$$

$$C_3H_7OH \text{ (l)} + 4\tfrac{1}{2}O_2 \text{ (g)} \rightarrow 3CO_2 \text{ (g)} + 4H_2O \text{ (l)}$$

a For the combustion of one mole of each alcohol, calculate i) the number of bonds of each type broken, ii) the number of bonds of each type formed, and complete a copy of Table 4.

b What is the difference, in terms of bonds broken and bonds formed, between the combustions of ethanol and propan-1-ol and between the combustions of propan-1-ol and butan-1-ol?

Table 4

Alcohol	Bonds broken/mol					Bonds formed	
	C—C	C—H	C—O	O—H	O=O	O=C	O—H
Ethanol							
Propan-1-ol							
Butan-1-ol							
Pentan-1-ol							
Hexan-1-ol							

c Use your answer to part **b** to complete Table 4 for two more alcohols, pentan-1-ol, $C_5H_{11}OH$, and hexan-1-ol, $C_6H_{13}OH$, which have very similar structural formulae to the others.

d Which of the bonds you have identified in part **b** are identical, i.e. bonds between the same atoms in identical molecules, and which are merely similar, i.e. bonds between the same atoms in different molecules?

e Would you expect a constant difference in $\Delta H^\ominus$ between one alcohol and the next in the list, i) at a temperature high enough for all reactants and products to be gaseous, ii) at 298 K? Hint: the difference in $\Delta H^\ominus_{vap}$ between one alcohol and the next is between 1 and 6 kJ mol^{-1}.

Now you can check your answer to Exercise 27 part **e**. You can either obtain the values from your data book or, if your teacher agrees, perform an experiment to determine the heats of combustion of a series of alcohols.

If you are going to do Experiment 4, you will find it helpful to look at the ILPAC video programme 'Using a Heat of Combustion Apparatus'.

If you are not doing the experiment, go directly to Exercise 28 on page 42.

EXPERIMENT 4   Determining enthalpies of combustion

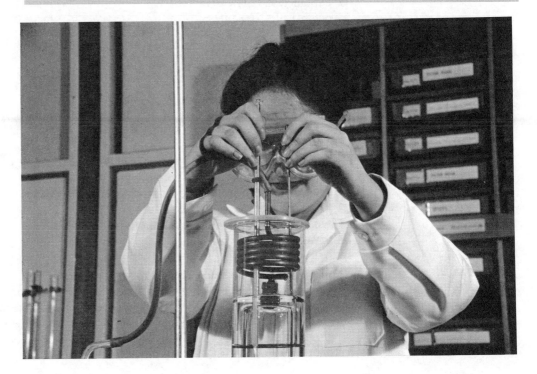

Aim   The purpose of this experiment is to determine the heats of combustion of a series of similar alcohols from butan-1-ol to octan-1-ol.

Introduction   In this experiment, you burn a measured mass of an alcohol in a spirit lamp and transfer the heat energy released to a calorimeter containing water. From the resulting temperature rise you can calculate the heat of combustion.

In your earlier calorimetric experiments, you assumed that **all** the heat energy released in a chemical reaction was absorbed by the contents of the calorimeter. You cannot make that assumption in this experiment for two reasons.

1. The heat energy is released in a flame, and although the apparatus is designed to transfer most of the energy to the calorimeter, a significant quantity is lost to the surrounding air.
2. The heat capacity of the calorimeter itself is **not** so small as to be insignificant compared with the heat capacity of its contents.

You can take account of both these factors by calibrating the apparatus using an alcohol with known heat of combustion.

Requirements   ■ safety spectacles
■ heat of combustion apparatus
■ spirit lamp
■ wood block
■ retort stand (with 2 clamps and bosses)

- Drechsel bottle
- filter pump
- rubber tubing (for connections to filter pump)
- water (at room temperature)
- adhesive labels
- propan-1-ol, C_3H_7OH
- butan-1-ol, C_4H_9OH
- pentan-1-ol, $C_5H_{11}OH$
- hexan-1-ol, $C_6H_{13}OH$
- heptan-1-ol, $C_7H_{15}OH$
- octan-1-ol, $C_8H_{17}OH$
- 6 beakers, 50 cm^3
- 6 teat pipette droppers
- Bunsen burner and protective mat
- wood splints
- tweezers (not plastic-tipped)
- balance (preferably capable of weighing to 0.001 g, but 0.01 g will do)
- thermometer −5 to −50°C (in 0.1°C)

(If these alcohols are supplied in separate spirit lamps, you will not need the next two items.)

HAZARD WARNING

The alcohols you will be using are highly flammable and are harmful by absorption through the skin and lungs. Therefore you **must**:
- **keep the stoppers on the bottles when not in use;**
- **keep the bottles away from flames;**
- **wash your hands after use (or wear gloves);**
- **wear safety spectacles.**

Procedure

Determination of the heat capacity of the apparatus

1. Arrange the heat of combustion apparatus (i.e. the calorimeter), the Drechsel bottle, etc., as shown in Fig. 10. Don't use the calorimeter base supplied by the manufacturer but stand the burner on a small block of wood to ensure a good flow of air. Adjust the height of the calorimeter (or the size of the block) so that the top of the spirit lamp is level with the bottom of the calorimeter.

Figure 10
Heat of combustion apparatus.

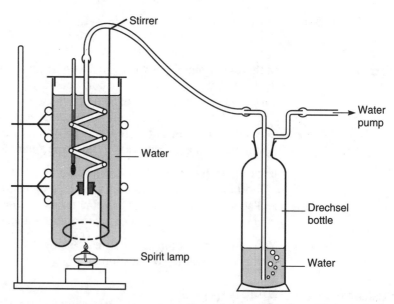

2. Use water at room temperature (not direct from the tap) to fill the calorimeter to about 1.5 cm below the rim. Mark this level with a label.
3. Pour a little propan-1-ol into a small beaker and use a teat pipette to half-fill the spirit lamp. (This may have been done for you already.) Replace the wick and

    cap, return any excess alcohol to the bottle, and remove both bottle and beaker to a safe distance from any flame.

4. Turn on the filter pump and adjust the flow of air through the Drechsel bottle to about 3–4 bubbles per second.

5. Stand the spirit lamp away from the calorimeter, and use a wood splint to light it. Adjust the height of the wick, using metal tweezers, to obtain a flame about 1 cm high.

6. Check that the lamp burns satisfactorily for about 15 seconds in position under the calorimeter. If it goes out, either increase the flow of air or adjust the height of the lamp relative to the calorimeter. Once these adjustments have been made, **they should not be changed** for the rest of the experiment. Extinguish the flame and put on the cap.

7. Weigh the spirit lamp, including the cap, as accurately as possible and record the mass in Results Table 3.

8. Stir the water in the calorimeter and record its temperature, to the nearest 0.1°C.

9. Put the lamp under the calorimeter and light it.

10. Slowly and continuously stir the water in the calorimeter and watch the thermometer. When the temperature has risen by about 10°C, extinguish the flame and immediately replace the cap. Keep stirring and record the maximum temperature of the water.

11. Re-weigh the spirit lamp and cap and record the mass.

12. Without removing the calorimeter from the stand, and holding **both together carefully**, pour away the water.

13. If you have time, repeat the experiment to increase the accuracy of your calibration. This second run should be much quicker because you should not need to make any adjustments (i.e. omit steps 1 and 3–6).

14. Before doing any calculations, repeat the experiment using as many of the other alcohols as you have time for and complete Results Table 4. If you have to use the same spirit lamp, you will have to empty it, rinse it with the new alcohol, and fit a new wick (or dry the old wick). If time is limited, your teacher may suggest that you share your results with other students, or may give you some pre-determined results.

Results Table 3

	1st run	2nd run	
Molar mass of propan-1-ol, M			$g\ mol^{-1}$
Initial mass of spirit lamp + alcohol, m_1			g
Final mass of spirit lamp + alcohol, m_2			g
Mass of alcohol burned, $m_1 - m_2$			g
Amount of alcohol burned, $n = (m_1 - m_2)/M$			mol
Initial temperature of calorimeter			°C
Final temperature of calorimeter			°C
Temperature change, ΔT			K
$\Delta H_c^{\ominus}$ [propan-1-ol] (given)		−2017	$kJ\ mol^{-1}$

Heat released during the experiment, ΔH
   = $\Delta H_c^{\ominus}$ [propan-1-ol] × amount burned
   = −2017 kJ mol^{-1} × n
			kJ

Heat required for a rise in temperature of 1 K $= \dfrac{\Delta H}{\Delta T} = C$, the calorimeter calibration factor			$kJ\ K^{-1}$
Average value of C			$kJ\ K^{-1}$

    (Specimen results on page 90.)

Results Table 4

	C$_4$H$_9$OH	C$_5$H$_{11}$OH	C$_6$H$_{13}$OH	C$_7$H$_{15}$OH	C$_8$H$_{17}$OH
Molar mass, M/g mol^{-1}					
Initial mass of lamp/g					
Final mass of lamp/g					
Mass of alcohol burned/g					
Amount burned, n/mol					
Initial temperature/°C					
Final temperature/°C					
Temperature change, ΔT/K					
$\Delta H_c = \dfrac{C \times \Delta T}{n}$ /kJ mol^{-1}					

(Specimen results on page 91.)

You can make use of your experimental results in the next exercise.

EXERCISE 28

Answers on page 91

a Using either your experimental results or $\Delta H^{\ominus}$ values from your data book, fill in the second column of Table 5.

Table 5

Alcohol	$\Delta H_c^{\ominus}$/kJ mol^{-1}	Differences/kJ mol^{-1}
propan-1-ol, C$_3$H$_7$OH		
butan-1-ol, C$_4$H$_9$OH		
pentan-1-ol, C$_5$H$_{11}$OH		
hexan-1-ol, C$_6$H$_{13}$OH		
heptan-1-ol, C$_7$H$_{15}$OH		
octan-1-ol, C$_8$H$_{17}$OH		
	Average difference =	

b Calculate the differences and fill in the third column. Calculate the average difference in $\Delta H_c^{\ominus}$.

c Do you now think it is reasonable to use average bond energy terms for C—C and C—H in the different alcohols? Explain your answer.

Having established that a particular kind of bond has a particular quantity of energy associated with it, we can calculate two average bond energies, $\overline{E}$(C—H) and $\overline{E}$(C—C), by solving simultaneous equations.

■ 5.2 Determining two bond energy terms simultaneously

Work through the following Revealing Exercise where we show you how to do this calculation. You need the following information:

butane: $\quad$ C$_4$H$_{10}$ (g) → 4C (g) + 10H (g); $\quad \Delta H^{\ominus} = +5165$ kJ mol^{-1}

pentane: $\quad$ C$_5$H$_{12}$ (g) → 5C (g) + 12H (g); $\quad \Delta H^{\ominus} = +6337$ kJ mol^{-1}

Q1 How many bonds are broken in the atomisation of butane and pentane?

A1 In butane, 3 C—C bonds and 10 C—H bonds are broken per molecule; in pentane, 4 C—C bonds and 12 C—H bonds are broken per molecule.

Q2 Express the enthalpy changes for the atomisation of pentane and butane as the sums of the bond energy terms.

A2 Butane: $3\overline{E}$(C—C) + $10\overline{E}$(C—H) = +5165 kJ mol^{-1}
Pentane: $4\overline{E}$(C—C) + $12\overline{E}$(C—H) = +6337 kJ mol^{-1}

Notice that for a compound, $\Delta H^{\ominus}_{\text{at}}$ refers to one mole of molecules, whereas for an element it refers to one mole of **atoms**.

Q3 Let $\overline{E}$ (C—C) = x kJ mol^{-1}
 $\overline{E}$ (C—H) = y kJ mol^{-1}
and solve these equations simultaneously.

A3 $3x + 10y = 5165$ (1)
$4x + 12y = 6337$ (2)
Multiply equation (1) by 4 and equation (2) by 3 and subtract:
$12x + 40y = 20660$
$12x + 36y = 19001$
 $4y = 1649 \therefore y = 412.25$
Substitute this value for y into either equation (1) or (2).
$3x + 10(412.25) = 5165$
$3x = 5165 - 4122.5 = 1042.5$ $\therefore x = 347.5$
$\therefore \overline{E}$(C—C) = **347.5 kJ mol**$^{-1}$, $\overline{E}$(C—H) = **412.2 kJ mol**$^{-1}$

Now that we have shown you how bond energy terms can be obtained we illustrate their use in estimating enthalpy changes in reactions for which there are no experimental data.

■ 5.3 Using bond energy terms to estimate enthalpy changes

In order to obtain a bond energy term which can be tabulated and used generally, an average value is taken for a particular type of bond in a large number of compounds. The bond energy terms quoted in your data book should, therefore, not be considered as accurately stating the bond energy in any particular molecular environment. Calculations using bond energy terms can give, therefore, only approximate answers.

OBJECTIVE   When you have finished this section you should be able to:
■ use bond energy terms to estimate enthalpy changes that cannot be determined directly.

You have already used one method for calculating enthalpy changes that cannot be determined directly, by substituting known enthalpy data into an energy cycle and applying Hess' law. We now show you another method, this time using bond energy terms, in a Worked Example. We remind you that:

> **Bond breaking requires energy (endothermic)**
>
> **Bond making releases energy (exothermic)**

WORKED EXAMPLE   Use bond energy terms to calculate the enthalpy change for the reaction:

$$CH_4 \text{ (g)} + Cl_2 \text{ (g)} \rightarrow CH_3Cl \text{ (g)} + HCl \text{ (g)}$$

Solution   1. Write the equation using structural formulae:

2. List the bonds broken and bonds made under the equations as shown:

bonds broken	bonds made
C — H	C — Cl
Cl — Cl	H — Cl

3. Look up the bond energy terms for the bonds broken and made. Add them up as shown, including negative signs for the exothermic bond-making.

bonds broken   bonds made

$\overline{E}$ (C—H) = 435 kJ mol^{-1}	$-\overline{E}$ (C—Cl) = −339 kJ mol^{-1}
$\overline{E}$ (Cl—Cl) = 242 kJ mol^{-1}	$-\overline{E}$ (H—Cl) = −431 kJ mol^{-1}
Total = 677 kJ mol^{-1}	Total = −770 kJ mol^{-1}

4. Add the values for bond breaking and making (including the correct signs) to obtain the required enthalpy change

$$\Delta H^{\ominus} = 677 \text{ kJ mol}^{-1} - 770 \text{ kJ mol}^{-1} = -93 \text{ kJ mol}^{-1}$$

5. Write the complete thermochemical equation

$$CH_4\,(g) + Cl_2\,(g) \rightarrow CH_3Cl\,(g) + HCl\,(g); \quad \Delta H^{\ominus} = \textbf{--93 kJ mol}^{-1}$$

The following energy-level diagram summarises the energy changes during the reaction we have just considered.

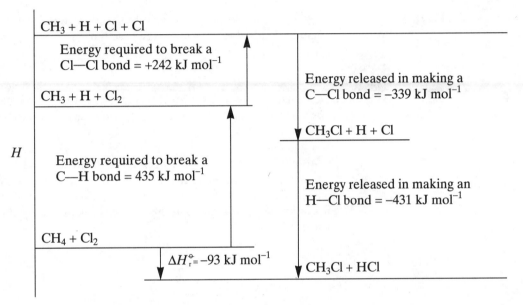

Now attempt the following exercises, two of which are A-level questions.

EXERCISE 29
Answers on page 91

Use bond energy terms listed in your data book to calculate the enthalpy change for the reactions
a $H_2\,(g) + Cl_2\,(g) \rightarrow 2HCl\,(g)$
b $N_2\,(g) + 3H_2\,(g) \rightarrow 2NH_3\,(g)$

EXERCISE 30
Answers on page 92
Table 6

Some bond energy terms are listed below:

Bond	H—H	C—H	C—Br	C—C	C=C	Br—Br
Bond energy /kJ mol^{-1}	435	415	284	356	598	193

a What do you understand by **bond energy term**?
b Using the given data, calculate the enthalpies of formation, from gaseous atoms, of
   i) gaseous propene.

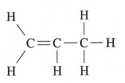

ii) gaseous 1,2-dibromopropane

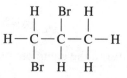

c Calculate the enthalpy change, ΔH°, for the reaction

$$CH_2{=}CH{-}CH_3 \text{ (g)} + Br_2 \text{ (g)} \rightarrow CH_2BrCHBrCH_3 \text{ (g)}$$

EXERCISE 31

Answers on page 92

a Use the values of bond energy terms contained in your data book to calculate the standard enthalpy change for the reaction

$$C_2H_6 \text{ (g)} + Cl_2 \text{ (g)} \rightarrow C_2H_5Cl \text{ (g)} + HCl \text{ (g)}$$

b Calculate another value for this standard enthalpy change from heats of formation.
c Write a short account of the reasons why the two values you have calculated differ from each other.

So far in Part B your work has been confined to covalent compounds. You have seen how to use bond energy terms to calculate the enthalpy change of formation of a molecular compound from its constituent gaseous atoms – an important step in the calculation of ΔH° for a reaction. Now we look at energy changes in the formation of ionic compounds.

LATTICE ENERGY (LATTICE ENTHALPY)

It is often useful to know the enthalpy of formation of an ionic compound from its constituent gaseous ions. The energy value is called the 'lattice energy' of the compound, because ionic bonding always leads to a solid crystal lattice. It provides a measure of the strength of ionic bonds.

OBJECTIVE   When you have finished this chapter you should be able to:
■ define **lattice energy**.

The lattice energy of an ionic compound is the enthalpy change which occurs when one mole of it is formed, as a crystal lattice, from its constituent gaseous ions.

This definition of lattice energy always gives a negative sign, e.g.

$$Na^+ (g) + Cl^- (g) \rightarrow Na^+Cl^- (s); \quad \Delta H^{\ominus}_{lat} = -781 \text{ kJ mol}^{-1}$$

If we were considering the energy required to separate the salt into its separate ions then the enthalpy change must have a positive sign:

$$Na^+Cl^- (s) \rightarrow Na^+ (g) + Cl^- (g); \quad \Delta H^{\ominus}_{lat} = +781 \text{ kJ mol}^{-1}$$

You may find that some books quote positive values of lattice energy, but you will not go wrong if you always relate $\Delta H^{\ominus}$ to the appropriate equation.

Since it is impossible to determine lattice energies directly by experiment we use an indirect method where we construct an energy diagram called a Born–Haber cycle.

■ 6.1 Calculating lattice energy using a Born–Haber cycle

The Born–Haber cycle is yet another application of Hess' law but the alternative routes involve more steps than you have used so far.

To construct a Born–Haber cycle you need two enthalpy changes not previously mentioned in this volume, ionisation energy and electron affinity. You should be familiar with ionisation energy from ILPAC Volume 1, Atomic Structure.

$\Delta H^{\ominus}_i$ **The ionisation energy of an element** is the enthalpy change which occurs when one mole of its gaseous atoms loses one mole of electrons to form one mole of gaseous positive ions, e.g.

$$Na (g) \rightarrow Na^+ (g); \quad \Delta H^{\ominus}_i = +500 \text{ kJ mol}^{-1}$$

$\Delta H^{\ominus}_e$ **The electron affinity of an element** is the enthalpy change which occurs when one mole of its gaseous atoms accepts one mole of electrons to form one mole of gaseous negative ions, e.g.

$$Br (g) + e^- \rightarrow Br^- (g); \quad \Delta H^{\ominus}_e = -342 \text{ kJ mol}^{-1}$$

OBJECTIVES   When you have finished this chapter you should be able to:
■ construct a **Born–Haber cycle** for an ionic compound;
■ use a Born–Haber cycle to calculate the lattice energy for an ionic compound.

Find the section on the Born–Haber cycle in your textbook. Skim through it and then use it to help you with the Revealing Exercise which follows.

Below is a generalised Born–Haber cycle for an ionic compound.

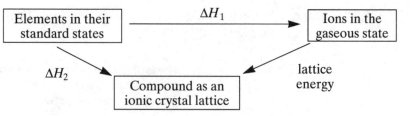

EXERCISE

Revealing

Q1 Redraw the cycle including the appropriate formulae for the formation of sodium chloride.

A1

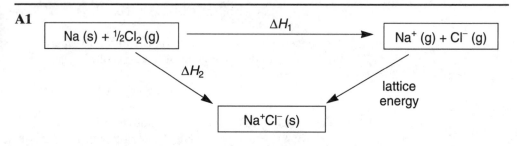

Q2 ΔH_1 is the sum of the energy change associated with four steps, two for sodium and two for chlorine. Write thermochemical equations for these four steps.

A2 $Na (s) \rightarrow Na (g)$; $\Delta H_{at}^{\ominus} = +108$ kJ mol^{-1}
$Na (g) \rightarrow Na^+ (g) + e^-$; $\Delta H_i^{\ominus} = +500$ kJ mol^{-1}
$\frac{1}{2}Cl_2 (g) \rightarrow Cl (g)$; $\Delta H_{at}^{\ominus} = +121$ kJ mol^{-1}
$Cl (g) + e^- \rightarrow Cl^- (g)$; $\Delta H_e^{\ominus} = -364$ kJ mol^{-1}

Q3 Calculate ΔH_1.

A3 $\Delta H_1 = \Delta H_{at}^{\ominus} (Na) + \Delta H_i^{\ominus}(Na) + \Delta H_{at}^{\ominus} (\frac{1}{2}Cl_2) + \Delta H_e^{\ominus} (Cl)$
So $\Delta H_1 = (+108 + 500 + 121 - 364)$ kJ mol^{-1} = $+365$ kJ mol^{-1}

Q4 What name is given to ΔH_2? Look up a value in your data book.

A4 ΔH_2 is the enthalpy change of formation of sodium chloride.
$\Delta H_f^{\ominus}[NaCl (s)] = -411$ kJ mol^{-1}

Q5 Insert the values for ΔH_1 and ΔH_2 in the energy cycle.

A5

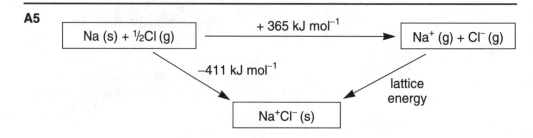

Q6   Use Hess' law to calculate the lattice energy for sodium chloride.

A6   365 kJ mol^{-1} + lattice energy = -411 kJ mol^{-1}
∴ lattice energy = -411 kJ mol^{-1} $-$ 365 kJ mol^{-1} = **-776 kJ mol^{-1}**

Born–Haber cycles are often drawn as energy-level diagrams. Compare the following energy-level diagram with the cycle you drew in the Revealing Exercise and trace the various steps.

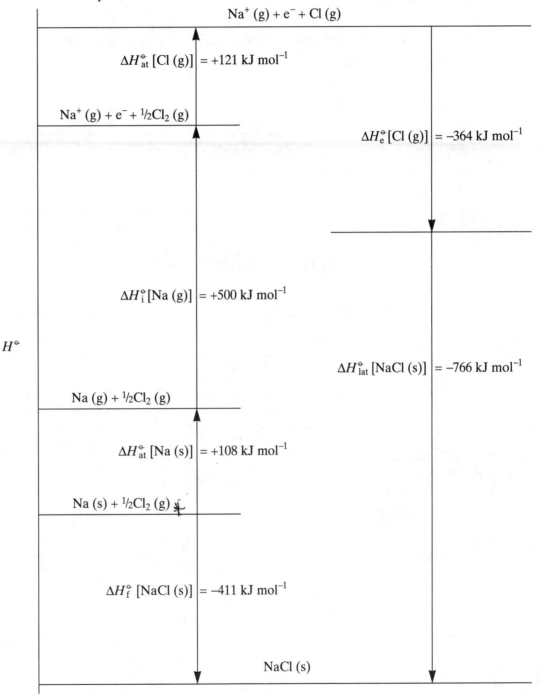

Born–Haber cycle for sodium chloride, drawn approximately to scale.

Note that Born–Haber cycles are frequently **not** drawn to scale, in order to save time and space. Also, the electrons are not always included in the ionisation steps.

Try drawing some Born–Haber cycles for yourself in the following exercises, and use the cycles to calculate some lattice energies.

EXERCISE 32
Answers on page 93

Draw a Born–Haber cycle for each of the following ionic compounds, and then calculate their lattice energies. (Note that in sodium hydride, the hydrogen forms a negative ion.) The cycles should be drawn as energy-level diagrams but need not be drawn to scale.

Table 7

| Compound | $\Delta H_f^{\ominus}$ /kJ mol^{-1} | Metal | | Non-metal | |
		$\Delta H_{at}^{\ominus}$ /kJ mol^{-1}	$\Delta H_i^{\ominus}$ /kJ mol^{-1}	$\Delta H_{at}^{\ominus}$ /kJ mol^{-1}	$\Delta H_e^{\ominus}$ /kJ mol^{-1}
KBr (K$^+$, Br$^-$)	−392	+89	+420	+112	−342
NaH (Na$^+$, H$^-$)	−57	+108	+500	+218	−72

EXERCISE 33
Answers on page 94

Complete Table 8 and draw Born–Haber cycles to obtain lattice energies. Note that in this example you may have to combine successive values for $\Delta H_i^{\ominus}$ and $\Delta H_e^{\ominus}$. Also, whereas $\Delta H_i^{\ominus}$ is **always** positive, $\Delta H_e^{\ominus}$ may be positive or negative.

Table 8

| Compound | $\Delta H_f^{\ominus}$ /kJ mol^{-1} | Metal | | Non-metal | |
		$\Delta H_{at}^{\ominus}$ /kJ mol^{-1}	$\Delta H_i^{\ominus}$ /kJ mol^{-1}	$\Delta H_{at}^{\ominus}$ /kJ mol^{-1}	$\Delta H_e^{\ominus}$ /kJ mol^{-1}
BaCl$_2$ (Ba^{2+}, 2Cl$^-$)	−860	+175	+500 +1000	+121	−364
SrO (Sr^{2+}, O^{2-})					

Born–Haber cycles are not used exclusively to calculate lattice energies, as the next two exercises illustrate. In particular, since it is difficult to obtain values of electron affinity by other methods, they are sometimes determined from Born–Haber cycles using values of lattice energy calculated from the laws of electrostatics.

EXERCISE 34
Answer on page 95

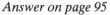

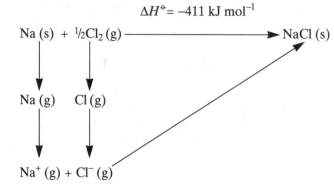

Use the above diagram and the following data to calculate $\Delta H^{\ominus}$ for the reaction:

$$Cl\,(g) + e^- \rightarrow Cl^-\,(g)$$

Na (s) → Na (g); $\Delta H^{\ominus} = 108$ kJ mol^{-1}
Na (g) → Na$^+$ (g) + e$^-$; $\Delta H^{\ominus} = 500$ kJ mol^{-1}
½Cl$_2$ (g) → Cl (g); $\Delta H^{\ominus} = 121$ kJ mol^{-1}
NaCl (s) → Na$^+$ (g) + Cl$^-$ (g); $\Delta H^{\ominus} = 776$ kJ mol^{-1}

EXERCISE 35
Answers on page 95

The Born–Haber cycle for the formation of calcium chloride is given below:

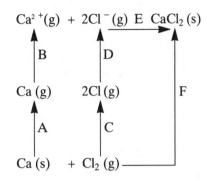

$A = 177$ kJ mol^{-1}, $C = 242$ kJ mol^{-1}, $F = -795$ kJ mol^{-1},
$B = 1690$ kJ mol^{-1}, $E = -2197$ kJ mol^{-1}.

a A is the enthalpy change of sublimation (atomisation) of solid calcium. Similarly, define the following:
  i) B,
  ii) C,
  iii) E,
  iv) F.
b Calculate the enthalpy change D.

Another use of Born–Haber cycles enables us to discuss the stoichiometry of compounds which might be formed by direct combination.

■ 6.2 Lattice energy and stoichiometry

We now use enthalpy data and suitable Born–Haber cycles to predict the formula of a compound.

OBJECTIVE When you have finished this section you should be able to:
■ predict the stoichiometry of a compound using calculated values of standard enthalpy of formation.

In the exercise which follows, you construct Born–Haber cycles for MgCl, MgCl$_2$ and MgCl$_3$ to determine enthalpy changes of formation and then decide which would be the most likely formula for magnesium chloride.

EXERCISE 36
Answers on page 96

a Construct Born–Haber cycles for MgCl, MgCl$_2$ and MgCl$_3$, inserting all the values except $\Delta H_f^\ominus$. Since experimentally determined lattice energies for MgCl and MgCl$_3$ are not available, use the theoretically calculated values:

$$\Delta H_{\text{lat}}^\ominus [\text{MgCl}] = -753 \text{ kJ mol}^{-1}$$

$$\Delta H_{\text{lat}}^\ominus [\text{MgCl}_3] = -5440 \text{ kJ mol}^{-1}$$

b Use the cycles to obtain values for
  i) $\Delta H_f^\ominus [\text{MgCl}]$,
  ii) $\Delta H_f^\ominus [\text{MgCl}_2]$,
  iii) $\Delta H_f^\ominus [\text{MgCl}_3]$.
c Which of the three compounds MgCl, MgCl$_2$, MgCl$_3$ is/are energetically stable with respect to the elements?

d Calculate the enthalpy change for the hypothetical reaction

$$2MgCl\ (s) \rightarrow MgCl_2\ (s) + Mg\ (s)$$

using the ΔH_f° values you calculated in part **b**.

e Discuss briefly the relative stability of MgCl and $MgCl_2$ in the light of your answer to **d**. Does this explain why MgCl is **not** known?

To test your understanding of the last section you should do the following Teacher-marked Exercise which is a question taken from a past A-level examination paper.

EXERCISE
Teacher-marked

Use your data book to determine the lattice energy of strontium chloride. Show how you arrive at your answer. A substance of formula $SrCl_3$ does not exist. What further energetics data would you need to explain this fact? Show how you would use the data.

Born–Haber cycles are also used to determine another quantity which cannot easily be measured directly – enthalpy of hydration, which we consider in the next chapter.

CHAPTER 7

ENTHALPY OF HYDRATION

Enthalpy of hydration is concerned with the bonding between dissolved ions and surrounding water molecules. It is closely related to two quantities you have already studied, lattice enthalpy and enthalpy of solution.

OBJECTIVES

When you have finished this chapter you should be able to:
- ■ define **enthalpy of hydration** for an ionic substance and for individual ions by means of thermochemical equations;
- ■ relate enthalpy of hydration to lattice enthalpy and enthalpy of solution by means of energy-level diagrams;
- ■ explain simply how enthalpy of hydration varies with ionic radius and charge.

Read about hydration of ions and enthalpy of hydration in your textbook(s) including, if necessary, your notes on enthalpy of solution and lattice enthalpy. You may find it helpful to refer to the diagram below, which shows what happens when an ionic salt dissolves in water. Then you should be able to do the following exercises.

Figure 11
(We have shown only one layer of attached water molecules surrounding each ion. There may be several layers, especially around small, highly charged ions.)

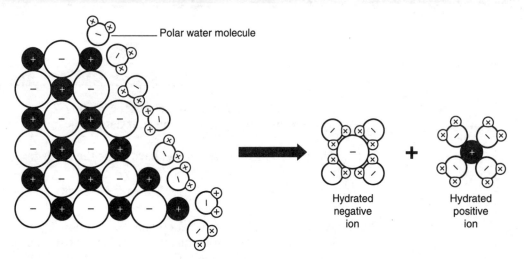

EXERCISE 37
Answers on page 97

a Write a thermochemical equation representing the complete separation of the ions in solid sodium chloride, including a value for $\Delta H^{\ominus}$ obtained from your data book.

b Write thermochemical equations representing the bonding of water molecules to the separated ions. Note that since we do not know precisely how many water molecules are attached, we write Na^+ (aq) rather than $Na(H_2O)_n{}^+$ for the hydrated ions, and put '+ aq' in the equation instead of '+ nH_2O'.

$$(\Delta H^{\ominus}_{hyd}(Na^+) \doteq -406 \text{ kJ mol}^{-1}; \quad \Delta H^{\ominus}_{hyd}(Cl^-) = -364 \text{ kJ mol}^{-1})$$

c Add together the equations you have written (in the same way as you add algebraic equations). What process does the resulting equation represent, and what is the value for $\Delta H^{\ominus}$?

In the next exercise you look at a similar process using an energy-level diagram.

EXERCISE 38

Answers on page 97

The following is an energy-level diagram for calcium chloride.

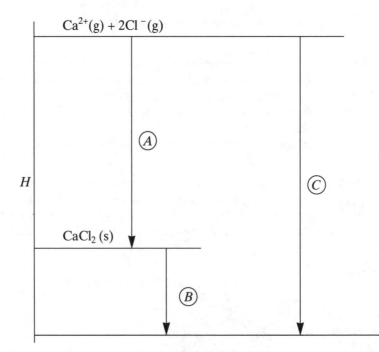

a What are the quantities denoted as *A*, *B* and *C*?

b Look up values of *A* and *C* in your data book and use them to calculate a value for *B*.

The preceding exercises should have made the following relationship clear to you:

$$\Delta H_{solution} = \Delta H_{hydration} - \Delta H_{lattice}$$

Also, you should realise that enthalpy of solution, because it is the small difference between two much larger quantities, can change from positive to negative with only relatively small variations in either lattice enthalpy or hydration enthalpy. This, of course, has some bearing on the solubility of ionic compounds, because most spontaneous changes have negative $\Delta H^{\ominus}$ values. You already know that this rule is not altogether reliable, so you should not be surprised to find some soluble substances with small **positive** values for ΔH_{sol}. Nevertheless, the following statement is generally true:

'The more negative the enthalpy of solution, the more soluble the substance.'

Although this is a useful guide, it is not quite the whole story, as you will discover when you compare the solubilities of a number of different salts in the unit on s-block elements in ILPAC Volume 4.

Now we look at the way in which enthalpy of hydration depends on ionic radius and charge.

■ 7.1 Variation of enthalpy of hydration with ionic radius and charge

Look at Table 9 which shows hydration enthalpies and ionic radii for a number of anions and cations. It will help you to do the exercise which follows.

Table 9

	Ionic radius/nm	$\Delta H_{hyd}^{\ominus}$/kJ mol^{-1}
Group I		
Li$^+$	0.060	−519
Na$^+$	0.095	−406
K$^+$	0.133	−322
Rb$^+$	0.148	−301
Cs$^+$	0.169	−276
Group II		
(Be^{2+})	0.031	−2450
Mg^{2+}	0.065	−1920
Ca^{2+}	0.099	−1650
Sr^{2+}	0.113	−1480
Ba^{2+}	0.135	−1380

EXERCISE 39

Answers on page 98

a From Table 9 find two pairs of ions of different charge in which the radius is almost the same. What is the effect on hydration enthalpy of varying the charge?

b What explanation can you give for your answer to **a**?

c For ions of the same charge, what is the effect on hydration enthalpy of increasing radius?

d What explanation can you give for your answer to **c**?

Precisely similar trends and explanations may be given for anions as well as cations.

Of course, a large ion (cation or anion) can accommodate a larger number of water molecules around its circumference but they are much less strongly held. Also, the electric field around a small ion is so strong that water molecules are held in several layers, so that the total number can be much greater than for a large ion. It is the combination of strength of bonding and total number of water molecules attached which determines the enthalpy of hydration.

In the next chapter we return to the experimental determination of enthalpy change of reaction and show you how to adapt for this purpose the titration method you learned in ILPAC Volume 1, The Mole.

8 THERMOMETRIC TITRATIONS

We now give you another method for determining experimentally the enthalpy change of a reaction, i.e. using the technique of thermometric titration.

OBJECTIVES

When you have finished this chapter you should be able to:
■ perform a **thermometric titration** in order to determine the enthalpy change of a reaction;
■ define standard **enthalpy change of neutralisation**.

In thermometric titrations we make use of the fate that reactions in solution are accompanied by temperature changes, and thus it is possible to follow the course of a reaction using a thermometer. In the next experiment you perform two thermometric titrations.

EXPERIMENT 5   A thermometric titration

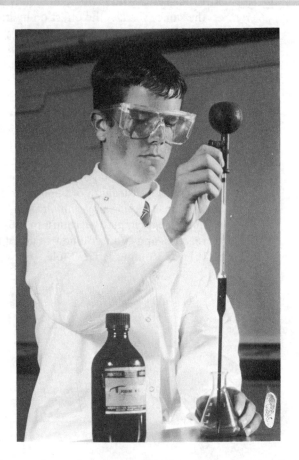

Aim

The purpose of this experiment is to determine the concentrations of two acids, hydrochloric acid, HCl, and ethanoic acid, CH_3CO_2H, by thermometric titration; and having done that, to calculate the enthalpy change for each reaction – the enthalpy change of neutralisation.

Introduction

You titrate both hydrochloric acid and ethanoic acid in turn with a standardised solution of sodium hydroxide and record the temperature of the mixtures during the course of the titrations. In each case a plot of temperature against time will enable you to determine the maximum temperature rise, from which you calculate both the concentration of the acid and the enthalpy change of neutralisation.

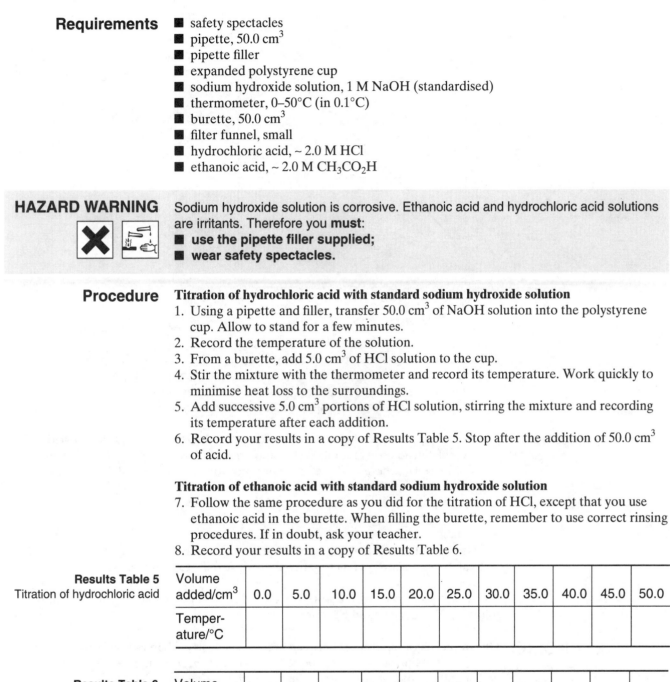

Requirements

- safety spectacles
- pipette, 50.0 cm³
- pipette filler
- expanded polystyrene cup
- sodium hydroxide solution, 1 M NaOH (standardised)
- thermometer, 0–50°C (in 0.1°C)
- burette, 50.0 cm³
- filter funnel, small
- hydrochloric acid, ~ 2.0 M HCl
- ethanoic acid, ~ 2.0 M CH_3CO_2H

HAZARD WARNING

Sodium hydroxide solution is corrosive. Ethanoic acid and hydrochloric acid solutions are irritants. Therefore you **must**:
- **use the pipette filler supplied;**
- **wear safety spectacles.**

Procedure

Titration of hydrochloric acid with standard sodium hydroxide solution
1. Using a pipette and filler, transfer 50.0 cm³ of NaOH solution into the polystyrene cup. Allow to stand for a few minutes.
2. Record the temperature of the solution.
3. From a burette, add 5.0 cm³ of HCl solution to the cup.
4. Stir the mixture with the thermometer and record its temperature. Work quickly to minimise heat loss to the surroundings.
5. Add successive 5.0 cm³ portions of HCl solution, stirring the mixture and recording its temperature after each addition.
6. Record your results in a copy of Results Table 5. Stop after the addition of 50.0 cm³ of acid.

Titration of ethanoic acid with standard sodium hydroxide solution
7. Follow the same procedure as you did for the titration of HCl, except that you use ethanoic acid in the burette. When filling the burette, remember to use correct rinsing procedures. If in doubt, ask your teacher.
8. Record your results in a copy of Results Table 6.

Results Table 5
Titration of hydrochloric acid

Volume added/cm³	0.0	5.0	10.0	15.0	20.0	25.0	30.0	35.0	40.0	45.0	50.0
Temper- ature/°C											

Results Table 6
Titration of ethanoic acid

Volume added/cm³	0.0	5.0	10.0	15.0	20.0	25.0	30.0	35.0	40.0	45.0	50.0
Temper- ature/°C											

Calculation
Specimen results on page 98

1. Plot temperature (*y*-axis) against volume of acid added (*x*-axis) for each acid on the same graph.
2. Extrapolate the curves as shown in Fig. 12. The point at which they meet corresponds to both the volume of acid required for neutralisation and to the maximum temperature.

Figure 12

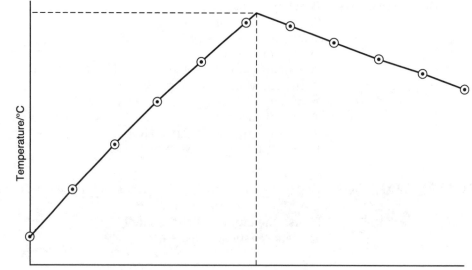

Volume of acid added/cm³

3. Calculate the concentration of each of the acids. If necessary, look at your notes in the mole unit of ILPAC Volume 1 to help you.
4. From the maximum temperature rise, determine the quantity of energy released in each titration. Assume that the specific heat capacity of the solutions is the same as that for water, 4.18 kJ kg⁻¹ K⁻¹ and that the heat capacity of the cup is zero.
5. Calculate the standard enthalpy change of neutralisation for each reaction.

Questions

Answers on page 99

1. The enthalpy change of neutralisation for a very dilute strong acid (i.e. an acid which is completely ionised in solution) reacting with a very dilute strong base is constant at −57.6 kJ mol⁻¹, where mol⁻¹ refers to one mole of water produced. Why is the value constant?
2. Experimental results for hydrochloric acid are usually a little less negative than −57.6 kJ mol⁻¹. Suggest two reasons for this.
3. Ethanoic acid is a weak acid, i.e. it is not completely ionised in solution. Suggest a reason why the enthalpies of neutralisation for reactions involving weak acids and/or weak bases are always less negative than for strong acids and bases.

As an aid to summarising the work you have done so far, we suggest you attempt the following Teacher-marked Exercise.

EXERCISE

Teacher-marked

One of the major differences between present chemistry syllabuses and those of some years ago is in the emphasis now placed on *thermochemistry*. Summarise the advantages and limitations of an understanding of energetics in chemistry. You may wish to consider, as part of your answer, how deductions can be made from enthalpy level diagrams, the use of mean bond enthalpy values and how enthalpy changes for such reactions as organic combustions and reactions in solution could be predicted.

In the final chapter of this volume, we take you a little further in your study of free energy change, ΔG, which you first encountered at the end of Part A. Syllabus requirements vary widely in this area; we therefore suggest that, before you start this chapter, you ask your teacher which parts of it are relevant to your study. While some of the ideas are simple, others are more difficult to grasp; consequently, your teacher may recommend that you spend only a short time on this section now and return to it at a later stage in your course.

THE DIRECTION OF CHANGE

You have already learned that the use of $\Delta H^{\ominus}$ to predict the stability of substances and the direction of change is useful but not completely reliable. It is $\Delta G^{\ominus}$ rather than $\Delta H^{\ominus}$ which is always negative for a reaction which goes to completion. We now show you how $\Delta H^{\ominus}$ and $\Delta G^{\ominus}$ are related to each other.

OBJECTIVES   When you have finished this chapter you should be able to:
■ state the equation relating to $\Delta H^{\ominus}$ and $\Delta G^{\ominus}$;
■ state how the value of $\Delta G^{\ominus}$ determines the feasibility of a reaction.

Free energy and enthalpy, and also changes in these quantities, are related by the following equations

$$G = H - TS$$
$$\Delta G = \Delta H - T\Delta S$$

where S is another measurable (or calculable) thermodynamic property called entropy and T is the absolute temperature. Before we discuss entropy, however, we want to be sure that you understand the use of the symbol $^{\ominus}$ in this context.

ΔH, ΔG and ΔS refer to **any** change in a system. For a chemical reaction, this change may involve any amounts of reactants under any conditions and may also be a **partial** change into a mixture of reactants and products.

$\Delta H^{\ominus}$, $\Delta G^{\ominus}$ and $\Delta S^{\ominus}$ refer only to a **complete** change in a system from reactants to products as shown in an equation, where reactants and products are at the **same standard conditions** of temperature, pressure and concentration.

The simple rule that a spontaneous change in a system can only occur if $\Delta G < 0$ is, unfortunately, not always easy to apply because we have to work with tabulated values of $\Delta G^{\ominus}$, not ΔG. It is not strictly true that spontaneous change can only occur if $\Delta G^{\ominus} < 0$: it has been shown that although a reaction with a small positive value of $\Delta G^{\ominus}$ cannot proceed to completion, it **can** proceed towards an equilibrium mixture of reactants and products, because **that** change has a negative value of ΔG.

The following diagram shows how the possibility of change is related to values of ΔG and $\Delta G^{\ominus}$.

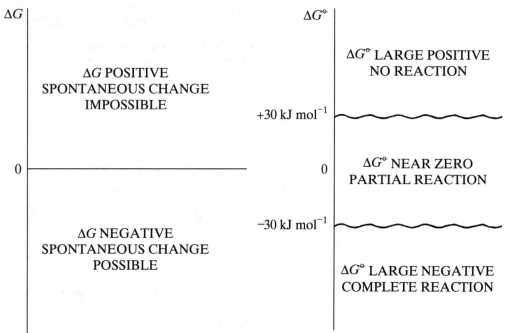

The boundary between partial reaction and complete reaction is, of course, not clearly defined. As $\Delta G^{\ominus}$ becomes more negative, reaction favours products more and more until, at values of $\Delta G^{\ominus}$ below about -30 kJ mol^{-1}, it can be regarded as complete.

Similarly, as $\Delta G^{\ominus}$ becomes more positive, reaction favours products less and less until, at values of $\Delta G^{\ominus}$ above about $+30$ kJ mol^{-1}, it can be regarded as not occurring at all.

You will learn more about incomplete changes, and the significance of the values ± 30 kJ mol^{-1}, in the ILPAC units on equilibrium. At this stage you should simply try to remember the following expressions:

$\Delta G < 0$ **spontaneous change possible**

$\Delta G^{\ominus} < 0$ **reaction possible; products favoured**

$\Delta G^{\ominus} < \sim -30$ **kJ mol^{-1} complete reaction possible**

$\Delta G^{\ominus} = \Delta H^{\ominus} - T\Delta S^{\ominus}$

The following sections on entropy will help you to apply them.

■ 9.1 Entropy, *S*

The only completely satisfactory definition of entropy is a mathematical one, which you need not concern yourself with at A-level. However, the definition does allow the calculation of absolute values of entropy for any amount of any substance. Non-mathematical definitions are imprecise, but you may find the following statements help you (eventually!) to get some mental picture of entropy.

1. Entropy is an indication of the degree of disorder in a system.
2. Entropy is a measure of the extent to which energy is dispersed.
3. Entropy is a measure of 'sameness', i.e. substances with high entropy are more nearly alike than those with low entropy.

It is a fundamental law of experience that entropy tends to increase in natural processes. Applying this to the three statements gives:

1. Disorder tends to increase.
2. Energy tends to become dispersed.
3. Things that are different tend to become less distinguishable.

Clearly it is possible for us to create order, to localise energy and to separate mixtures, all of which **decrease** the entropy of a system, but we believe this can only be done at the expense of a greater increase in the entropy of the surroundings. This means that in the passage of any interval of time

$\Delta S\text{(total)} > 0$

You may like to reflect on the philosophical significance of this statement as regards the nature of time and the future of our universe. (Does it mean that we are inexorably moving towards a state of maximum entropy where energy and atoms are totally and randomly dispersed – the so-called 'heat-death'?) However, it is of more relevance to your A-level studies to focus on entropy changes within a defined system. Since

$\Delta S\text{(total)} = \Delta S\text{(system)} + \Delta S\text{(surroundings)}$

we can say that

$\Delta S\text{(system)} + \Delta S\text{(surroundings)} > 0$

and therefore that, in many cases, $\Delta S\text{(system)} > 0$.

Thus, just as the enthalpy of a reacting system often (but not always) decreases ($\Delta H^\ominus$ negative), so the entropy often increases ($\Delta S^\ominus$ positive).

OBJECTIVES

When you have finished this section you should be able to:
■ explain, in simple terms, the differences in **entropy** between solids and liquids, and between liquids and gases;
■ state whether the **standard entropy change** for a given reaction is positive or negative.

Read about entropy in your textbook(s). Don't worry if you still feel a little uncertain about the nature of entropy. The way you **use** values of entropy is very simple, and when you have mastered that, you may wish to return to your textbook and also re-read the preceding pages of this unit.

Now try the next two exercises.

EXERCISE 40
Answer on page 99

Does the entropy of a substance increase or decrease when its temperature is raised? Explain your answer.

EXERCISE 41
Answers on page 99

Look up and record the values of $S^\ominus$ at 298 K for the following substances:
a iodine (s),
b bromine (l),
c chlorine (g),
d water (l),
e water (g).

Whenever you use tables of entropy, you should bear in mind three points.

1. The tabulated entropy values give the entropy of one mole of substance in its standard state.
2. The unit is J K^{-1} mol^{-1} (not kJ K^{-1} mol^{-1}).
3. These are actual entropy values, not entropy changes.

If we can look up entropy values for reactants and products, it is a simple matter to calculate $\Delta S^\ominus$, but first we consider how to predict whether $\Delta S^\ominus$ is positive or negative without reference to tables.

■ 9.2 Predicting entropy changes

We consider five examples.

1. $2Cu\ (s) + O_2\ (g) \rightarrow 2CuO\ (s)$

   Gases have much higher values of entropy than solids because they are less ordered and energy is more dispersed. The conversion of gas to solid, as in this example, is therefore accompanied by a large decrease in entropy.

2. $2H_2\ (g) + O_2\ (g) \rightarrow 2H_2O\ (l)$

   Here there is a large decrease in entropy because three moles of gas form two moles of liquid. Liquids have lower values of entropy because they are more ordered and energy is more localised.

3. $2H_2\ (g) + O_2\ (g) \rightarrow 2H_2O\ (g)$

   Here there is a decrease in entropy because three moles of gas form two moles and the system becomes more ordered. However, the entropy decrease is not so great as in example 2.

4. N_2O_4 (g) → $2NO_2$ (g)

In this reaction, one mole of gas forms two moles of gas. Therefore, the entropy increases.

5. H_2O (l) → H_2O (g)

Here one mole of liquid forms one mole of gas. Therefore, the entropy increases.

To see if you can apply this to an examination question, try the next exercise.

EXERCISE 42
Answers on page 99

For each of the following reactions, indicate whether the entropy is likely to **increase**, **decrease** or **stay the same**, explaining your reasoning.
a H_2 (g) + C_2H_4 (g) → C_2H_6 (g)
b N_2 (g) + $3H_2$ (g) → $2NH_3$ (g)
c $2NaNO_3$ (s) → $2NaNO_2$ (s) + O_2 (g).

You can confirm the predictions made in the examples and in the exercise by calculating the entropy changes.

■ 9.3 Calculating entropy changes

OBJECTIVE

When you have finished this section you should be able to:
■ calculate $\Delta S^\ominus$ for a process from tabulated values of $S^\ominus$.

Because entropy is a function like enthalpy, we can calculate the entropy change for a process by the relation

$$\Delta S^\ominus = S^\ominus \text{ (products)} - S^\ominus \text{ (reactants)}$$

We illustrate this by a Worked Example.

WORKED EXAMPLE

Calculate the standard entropy change for the reaction

$$2Cu \text{ (s)} + O_2 \text{ (g)} → 2CuO \text{ (s)}$$

Solution

1. Look up the value of $S^\ominus$ for each substance, multiply it by the number of moles in the reaction, and put this value under the formula.

$$\begin{array}{cccc} & 2Cu \text{ (s)} & + \quad O_2 \text{ (g)} → & 2CuO \text{ (s)} \\ S^\ominus/\text{J K}^{-1} \text{ mol}^{-1} & (2 \times 33.3) & (204.9) & (2 \times 43.5) \end{array}$$

2. Calculate the total entropy of the products.

$$S^\ominus \text{ [products]} = 2 \times 43.5 \text{ J K}^{-1} \text{ mol}^{-1} = 87.0 \text{ J K}^{-1} \text{ mol}^{-1}$$

3. Calculate the total entropy of the reactants.

$$S^\ominus \text{ [reactants]} = [(2 \times 33.3) + 204.9] \text{ J K}^{-1} \text{ mol}^{-1} = 271.5 \text{ J K}^{-1} \text{ mol}^{-1}$$

4. Calculate the entropy change by subtraction.

$$\Delta S^\ominus = S^\ominus \text{ [products]} - S^\ominus \text{ [reactants]} = (87.0 - 271.5) \text{ J K}^{-1} \text{ mol}^{-1}$$
$$= \mathbf{-184.5 \text{ J K}^{-1} \text{ mol}^{-1}}$$

Now work out some values of $\Delta S^\ominus$ for yourself.

EXERCISE 43
Answers on page 100

Calculate $\Delta S^{\ominus}$ for the reactions in Exercise 42.

EXERCISE 44
Answers on page 100

Predict whether $\Delta S^{\ominus}$ will be positive or negative for each of the following reactions. In at least one example, check your prediction by calculation.

a $CO\ (g) + Cl_2\ (g) \rightarrow COCl_2\ (g)$
b $2H_2O_2\ (l) \rightarrow 2H_2O\ (l) + O_2\ (g)$
c $C_2H_4\ (g) + 3O_2\ (g) \rightarrow 2CO_2\ (g) + 2H_2O\ (l)$
d $2KClO_3\ (s) \rightarrow 2KCl\ (s) + 3O_2\ (g)$
e $2C\ (s) + O_2\ (g) \rightarrow 2CO\ (g)$

Now that you know how to calculate $\Delta S^{\ominus}$, you can use the value to calculate $\Delta G^{\ominus}$ in order to see whether or not a reaction is possible.

■ 9.4 Using $\Delta S^{\ominus}$ to calculate $\Delta G^{\ominus}$

You already know that the standard free energy change, $\Delta G^{\ominus}$, is related to enthalpy and entropy changes by the equation

$$\Delta G^{\ominus} = \Delta H^{\ominus} - T\Delta S^{\ominus}$$

and that, for a reaction to be possible, $\Delta G^{\ominus}$ must be substantially negative. We now show you how to predict the feasibility of a reaction by calculating $\Delta G^{\ominus}$.

OBJECTIVES

When you have finished this section you should be able to:
■ calculate $\Delta G^{\ominus}$ for a process, given tables of $\Delta H^{\ominus}$ and $S^{\ominus}$ values;
■ use calculated values of $\Delta G^{\ominus}$ to determine if a process is possible.

We start with a Worked Example.

WORKED EXAMPLE

Calculate the standard free energy change, $\Delta G^{\ominus}$, for the process

$$CaO\ (s) + H_2O\ (l) \rightarrow Ca(OH)_2\ (s)$$

at 25°C, using the following values of standard enthalpy of formation and entropy.

Table 10

	$\Delta H_f^{\ominus}$/kJ mol^{-1}	$S^{\ominus}$/J K^{-1} mol^{-1}
CaO (s)	−635.5	39.7
Ca(OH)$_2$ (s)	−986.6	76.1
H$_2$O (l)	−285.9	70.0

Solution

1. Calculate the standard enthalpy change.
   $\Delta H^{\ominus} = \Delta H_f^{\ominus}[\text{products}] - \Delta H_f^{\ominus}[\text{reactants}]$
   $\quad = -986.6 \text{ kJ mol}^{-1} - (-635.5 - 285.9) \text{ kJ mol}^{-1}$
   $\quad = (-986.6 + 921.4) \text{ kJ mol}^{-1} = -65.2 \text{ kJ mol}^{-1}$

2. Calculate the standard entropy change.
   $\Delta S^{\ominus} = S^{\ominus}[\text{products}] - S^{\ominus}[\text{reactants}]$
   $\quad = 76.1 \text{ J K}^{-1} \text{ mol}^{-1} - (39.7 + 70.0) \text{ J K}^{-1} \text{ mol}^{-1}$
   $\quad = -33.6 \text{ J K}^{-1} \text{ mol}^{-1} = -0.0336 \text{ kJ K}^{-1} \text{ mol}^{-1}$
   Note the change of unit from J to kJ. This is necessary for the next step.

3. Substitute into the expression for $\Delta G^\ominus$.

$\Delta G^\ominus = \Delta H^\ominus - T\Delta S^\ominus$
$= -65.2 \text{ kJ mol}^{-1} - (298 \text{ K} \times -0.0336 \text{ kJ K}^{-1} \text{ mol}^{-1})$
$= (-65.2 + 10.0) \text{ kJ mol}^{-1} = \mathbf{-55.2 \text{ kJ mol}^{-1}}$

The negative value of $\Delta G^\ominus$ indicates that at 25°C and 1.00 atm, this reaction can proceed spontaneously (although it **may**, of course, be slow).

Now try some similar calculations for yourself.

EXERCISE 45

Answers on page 100

Calculate the standard free energy change, $\Delta G^\ominus$, accompanying each of the following processes at 25°C.

a $2NO (g) + O_2 (g) \rightarrow N_2O_4 (g)$
b $NH_3 (g) + HCl (g) \rightarrow NH_4Cl (s)$
c $H_2O (l) \rightarrow H_2O (g)$

You may have realised that it would have been simpler to calculate $\Delta G^\ominus$ in the last exercise using the expression you met in Part A.

$$\Delta G^\ominus = \Sigma \Delta G_f^\ominus [\text{products}] - \Sigma \Delta G_f^\ominus [\text{reactants}]$$

However, the great advantage of using $\Delta H^\ominus$ and $\Delta S^\ominus$ is that you can calculate $\Delta G^\ominus$ at temperatures other than 298 K as we show in the next section.

■ 9.5 Temperature and spontaneous processes

You would expect $\Delta G^\ominus$ to vary considerably with temperature because of the form of the equation

$$\Delta G^\ominus = \Delta H^\ominus - T\Delta S^\ominus$$

This variation means that some processes which are not possible at low temperatures become feasible at higher temperatures, and vice versa. For an example, consider the familiar process

$$H_2O (l) \rightarrow H_2O (g)$$

You know that this change does not occur to completion (in a closed system) at 25°C but that it proceeds spontaneously at temperatures above 100°C. This shows that $\Delta G^\ominus$ has very different values at different temperatures.

OBJECTIVES

When you have finished this section you should be able to:
■ calculate $\Delta G^\ominus$ for a stated reaction at any temperature;
■ explain why many endothermic reactions are possible only at high temperatures.

Note that the variation of $\Delta G^\ominus$ with temperature is quite separate from the fact that an increase in temperature increases the **rate** of reaction. Remember that thermodynamics tells us nothing at all about how fast a feasible reaction will occur.

To calculate $\Delta G^\ominus$ at a temperature other than 25°C we should, strictly speaking, use values of $\Delta H^\ominus$ and $\Delta S^\ominus$ at the appropriate temperature. Fortunately, the variation of $\Delta H^\ominus$ and $\Delta S^\ominus$ with temperature is small enough for us to ignore in this context.

EXERCISE 46
Answers on page 100

Calculate $\Delta G^{\ominus}$ (1000 K) for the following reactions and compare with given values of $\Delta G^{\ominus}$ (298 K). State whether or not the reactions are feasible at each temperature.

a $2NO\ (g) + O_2\ (g) \rightarrow N_2O_4\ (g)$; $\Delta G^{\ominus}(298\ K) = -75.6$ kJ mol^{-1}

b $NH_3\ (g) + HCl\ (g) \rightarrow NH_4Cl\ (s)$; $\Delta G^{\ominus}(298\ K) = -92.3$ kJ mol^{-1}

c $H_2O\ (l) \rightarrow H_2O\ (g)$; $\Delta G^{\ominus}(298\ K) = +8.6$ kJ mol^{-1}

d $CaCO_3\ (s) \rightarrow CaO\ (s) + CO_2\ (g)$; $\Delta G^{\ominus}(298\ K) = +130.2$ kJ mol^{-1}

(If your data book gives values for different forms of $CaCO_3$, use those for calcite.)

EXERCISE 47
Answers on page 101

a In what circumstances can an endothermic reaction take place spontaneously?

b Explain why, in the majority of cases, $\Delta H^{\ominus}$ provides an indication of the feasibility of a reaction at 298 K.

In the rest of your course, you will often use $\Delta H^{\ominus}$ as an indication of the stability of a substance, i.e. to indicate whether a certain reaction is likely to occur. You should now realise that $\Delta G^{\ominus}$ provides a better indication than $\Delta H^{\ominus}$ and should be used if data are available.

In order to consolidate your understanding of the use of $\Delta H^{\ominus}$ and $\Delta G^{\ominus}$ as guides to the feasibility of a reaction, your teacher may wish you to attempt the following Teacher-marked Exercise, which is taken from a Special Paper.

EXERCISE
Teacher-marked

'Not all exothermic reactions are spontaneous; some endothermic changes are spontaneous.'

Discuss the extent to which a knowledge of the enthalpy change for a reaction is a guide to its ability to proceed.

Illustrate your answer by considering **four** reactions of varied type, **two** of which are exothermic, and **two** endothermic.

You may wish to consider some or all of the following reactions or others of your own choice.

$$N_2O_4\ (g) \rightleftharpoons 2NO_2\ (g)$$

$$N_2\ (g) + 3H_2\ (g) \rightleftharpoons 2NH_3\ (g)$$

$$NH_4Cl\ (s) \rightleftharpoons NH_3\ (g) + HCl\ (g)$$

$$CaCO_3\ (s) \rightleftharpoons CaO\ (s) + CO_2\ (g)$$

■ End-of-unit test

To find out how well you have learned the material in this volume, try the test which follows. Read the notes below before starting.

1. You should spend about 1½–2 hours on this test.
2. You will need a sheet of graph paper and a data book.
3. Hand your answers to your teacher for marking.

Questions 1–3 concern an attempt to measure the enthalpy of neutralisation of hydrochloric acid with sodium hydroxide.

A student carefully measured out 45 cm³ of the standard 2 mol dm⁻³ hydrochloric acid and placed it in a suitable vessel. The steady temperature of the solution was noted. Five cm³ of standard sodium hydroxide was measured into a small beaker and then this was tipped into the hydrochloric acid. The maximum temperature was recorded after stirring the solution well. The whole experiment was repeated using different volumes of acid and alkali. The results are plotted graphically below. (The specific heat capacities of the solutions were taken as 4.18 J g⁻¹ °C⁻¹ and the densities of the solutions were assumed to be 1 g cm⁻³.)

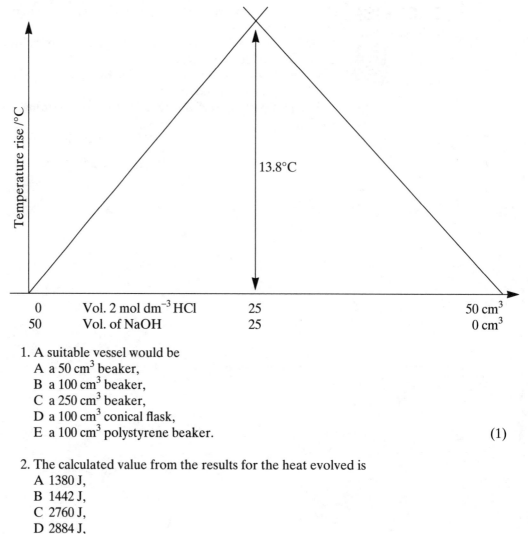

| 0 | Vol. 2 mol dm⁻³ HCl | 25 | 50 cm³ |
| 50 | Vol. of NaOH | 25 | 0 cm³ |

1. A suitable vessel would be
   A a 50 cm³ beaker,
   B a 100 cm³ beaker,
   C a 250 cm³ beaker,
   D a 100 cm³ conical flask,
   E a 100 cm³ polystyrene beaker.   (1)

2. The calculated value from the results for the heat evolved is
   A 1380 J,
   B 1442 J,
   C 2760 J,
   D 2884 J,
   E 5768 J.   (1)

3. The enthalpy of neutralisation of hydrochloric acid and sodium hydroxide when calculated from these results would be
A -27.6 kJ mol^{-1},
B -28.84 kJ mol^{-1},
C -55.2 kJ mol^{-1},
D -57.68 kJ mol^{-1},
E -115.37 kJ mol^{-1}. (1)

4. The energy evolved when one mole of gaseous calcium ions is hydrated according to the equation

$$Ca^{2+}(g) + aq \rightarrow Ca^{2+}(aq)$$

is greater than the corresponding value for barium ions (Ba^{2+}) because the
A ionisation energy of calcium is greater than that of barium,
B atomic radius of calcium is greater than that of barium,
C lattice energy of calcium oxide is greater than that of barium oxide,
D ionic radius of Ca^{2+} is less than that of Ba^{2+},
E solubility of calcium hydroxide in water is less than that of barium hydroxide. (1)

5. The standard enthalpy of formation of methane is given by

$$C(graphite) + 2H_2(g) \rightarrow CH_4(g)$$

$$\Delta H^{\ominus}_{298} = -74 \text{ kJ (mol methane)}^{-1}$$

The enthalpies of atomisation of graphite and hydrogen are given by

$$C(graphite) \rightarrow C(g) \qquad \Delta H^{\ominus} = +712 \text{ kJ mol}^{-1}$$

$$\tfrac{1}{2}H_2(g) \rightarrow H(g) \qquad \Delta H^{\ominus} = +215.5 \text{ kJ mol}^{-1}$$

The bond energy, in kJ mol^{-1}, of the C—H bond in methane is
A -590,
B -375,
C $+305$,
D $+375$,
E $+412$. (1)

6. For which equation is the enthalpy change in kJ mol^{-1} equal to the standard enthalpy of formation of water in kJ mol^{-1} at 298 K and 1 atm?
A $2H(g) + O(g) \rightarrow H_2O(l)$,
B $2H_2(g) + O_2(g) \rightarrow 2H_2O(l)$,
C $2H(g) + O(g) \rightarrow H_2O(g)$,
D $H_2(g) + O(g) \rightarrow H_2O(l)$,
E $H_2(g) + \tfrac{1}{2}O_2(g) \rightarrow H_2O(l)$. (1)

For each of the questions 7–10, **one** or **more** of the responses given is/are correct. Decide which of the responses is/are correct and then choose

A if **1, 2** and **3** are correct,
B if **1** and **2** only are correct,
C if **2** and **3** only are correct,
D if **1** only is correct,
E if **3** only is correct.

Directions summarised				
A	B	C	D	E
1, 2, 3	**1, 2**	**2, 3**	**1**	**3**
correct	only	only	only	only

7. Which of the following enthalpy values is/are required in order to calculate the mean bond enthalpy of the N—H bonds in NH_3 from the equation

$$N_2 \, (g) + 3H_2 \, (g) \rightarrow 2NH_3 \, (g)$$

1 The enthalpy of formation of NH_3.
2 The dissociation enthalpy of N_2.
3 The dissociation enthalpy of H_2. (1)

8. $LiCl \, (s) + aq \rightarrow Li^+ \, (aq) + Cl^- \, (aq)$

In calculating the enthalpy change for the above process, which of the following is (are) necessary?
1 Ionisation energy of lithium.
2 Electron affinity of chlorine.
3 Lattice energy of lithium chloride. (1)

9. When an ionic solid dissolves in water
1 energy is absorbed in the separation of the ions,
2 energy is released in the hydration of the ions,
3 the enthalpy of solution may be exothermic or endothermic. (1)

10.

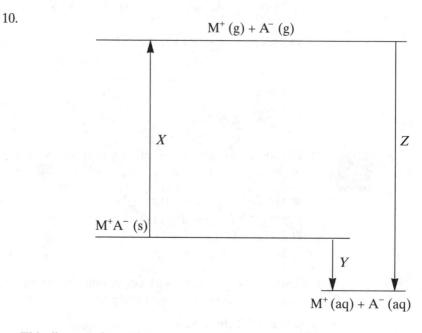

This diagram shows that
1 dissolving M^+A^- (s) is exothermic,
2 Z is the enthalpy of solution of M^+A^- (s),
3 X is the atomisation energy of M^+A^- (s). (1)

11. **a** State Hess' law. (2)
  b Define the terms
    i) enthalpy change of atomisation, ΔH_a (of an element),
    ii) enthalpy change of formation, ΔH_f. (4)
  c Given that
    $\Delta H_f^{\ominus}[NH_3 (g)] = -46.2 \text{ kJ mol}^{-1}$
    $\Delta H_a^{\ominus}[N_2 (g)] = +473 \text{ kJ mol}^{-1}$
    $\Delta H_a^{\ominus}[H_2 (g)] = +218 \text{ kJ mol}^{-1}$
    calculate the average N—H bond energy in ammonia. (3)

12. Coke (carbon), ethanol and hydrogen can all be used as fuels.
  a Write equations for the complete combustion of these fuels. (3)
  b Using the following standard enthalpies of formation,

    $\Delta H_f^{\ominus}/\text{kJ mol}^{-1}$: CO_2 (g), –394; H_2O (l), –286; C_2H_5OH (l), –278

    i) write down the standard enthalpy of combustion of coke,
    ii) calculate the standard enthalpy of combustion of ethanol. (4)
  c Use the data given below to calculate the standard enthalpy of combustion of hydrogen.
    Bond enthalpy term/kJ mol^{-1}: H—H, 436; O=O, 496; O—H, 463
    $\Delta H_{vap}^{\ominus}/\text{kJ mol}^{-1}$: H_2O (l), 41 (4)
  d i) Use your answers in **b** and **c** to calculate the energy evolved, in kJ g^{-1}, when each fuel is burned.
    (Relative atomic masses: H = 1, C = 12, O = 16.)
    ii) Comment on the advantages and disadvantages of hydrogen as a fuel. (5)

13. The following table lists the enthalpy changes of combustion of several monohydric alcohols.

Table 11

Alcohol	$\Delta H_c^{\ominus}/\text{kJ mol}^{-1}$
Methanol	–715
Ethanol	–1367
Propan-1-ol	–2017
Butan-1-ol	–2675

  a Draw a plot of $\Delta H_c^{\ominus}$ against the relative molecular mass of the alcohols. (3)
  b From your graph estimate a value for the enthalpy change of combustion of pentan-1-ol. (2)
  c Given $\Delta H_f^{\ominus}[H_2O (l)] = -286 \text{ kJ mol}^{-1}$ and $\Delta H_f^{\ominus}[CO_2 (g)] = -394 \text{ kJ mol}^{-1}$, calculate the standard enthalpy change of formation of ethanol. (3)
  d The enthalpy change of combustion of ethane-1,2-diol is –1180 kJ mol^{-1}. What would you expect the corresponding value for propane-1,3-diol to be? (1)

14. **a** Aluminium oxide and iron(III) oxide have the same type of crystal structure, but the lattice enthalpy of aluminium oxide is considerably greater than that of iron(III) oxide. Explain why the lattice enthalpies should differ in this way. (3)
  b Draw a Born–Haber cycle to show how the lattice enthalpy of a metal oxide M_2O_3 could be determined, clearly indicating the enthalpy terms involved in each stage of the cycle. (5)

15. **a** Some energy data are tabulated below.

Process	$\Delta H^\ominus$ (298 K)/kJ mol^{-1}
$Na\ (s) \rightarrow Na\ (g)$	+108
$\frac{1}{2}Cl_2\ (g) \rightarrow Cl\ (g)$	+121
$Na\ (g) \rightarrow Na^+\ (g) + e^-$	+496
$Cl\ (g) + e^- \rightarrow Cl^-$	−349
$Ca\ (g) \rightarrow Ca^{2+}\ (g) + 2e^-$	+1736
$Ca^{2+}\ (g) \rightarrow Ca^{3+}\ (g) + e^-$	+4941
$Ca^{2+}\ (g) + 2Cl^-\ (g) \rightarrow CaCl_2\ (s)$	−2220
$Ca^{3+}\ (g) + 3Cl^-\ (g) \rightarrow CaCl_3\ (s)$	−4800 (estimated)
$NaCl\ (s) \rightarrow Na^+\ (g) + Cl^-\ (g)$	+787
$NaCl\ (s) + water \rightarrow Na^+\ (aq) + Cl^-\ (aq)$	+4

Using this information,
i)   calculate the standard molar enthalpy change for the process

$$Na\ (s) + \frac{1}{2}Cl_2\ (g) \rightarrow Na^+\ (g) + Cl^-\ (g),$$

ii) explain why $CaCl_3$ (s) does not exist but $CaCl_2$ (s) does,
iii) comment on the difference between the values of the enthalpy change of
     lattice breaking of NaCl (s) and the enthalpy of solution of NaCl (s) in water
     and define a term which is useful in this context,
iv) discuss the process occurring at the molecular level when solid sodium chloride
     dissolves in water,
v)   calculate the standard enthalpy of formation of sodium chloride.   (11)
b State and discuss the general principles which govern the extent to which
compounds are soluble in water.   (4)

16. In an experiment to determine the enthalpy of neutralisation of sodium hydroxide
with sulphuric acid, 50 cm^3 of 0.40 M sodium hydroxide was titrated,
thermometrically, with 0.50 M sulphuric acid. The results were plotted as follows:

Figure 13

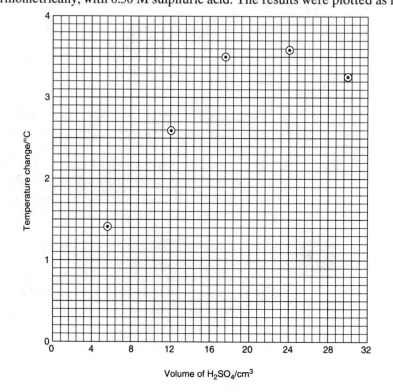

a Define 'enthalpy of neutralisation'. (2)

b What is a thermometric titration? (1)

c Describe, or draw a labelled diagram of, the apparatus you would use for such a titration. (2)

d How do you account for the shape of the graph? (2)

e Calculate a value for the enthalpy of neutralisation of sodium hydroxide with sulphuric acid. (The specific heat capacity of water is $4.2 \text{ J K}^{-1} \text{ g}^{-1}$.) What assumptions have you made in your calculations? (5)

17. **a** Calculate the standard entropy change and standard free energy change at 298 K accompanying the following process:

$$CO \text{ (g)} + Cl_2 \text{ (g)} \rightarrow COCl_2 \text{ (g)}; \Delta H^{\circ} = -112 \text{ kJ mol}^{-1}$$

given the following table of standard entropy values.

Table 12

Substance	$S^{\circ}/\text{J mol}^{-1} \text{ K}^{-1}$
CO (g)	198
COCl (g)	289
Cl₂ (g)	233

(4)

b Would you expect this reaction to be feasible i) at 298 K, and ii) at very high temperatures? (2)

(Total: 85 marks)

THE BOMB CALORIMETER

The apparatus and procedures you used to determine the enthalpy change of combustion in Experiment 4 are capable of giving reasonable but not highly accurate results. For more accurate results a bomb calorimeter is used.

OBJECTIVE When you have finished this appendix you should be able to:
■ describe the **bomb calorimeter**.

For a description of the bomb calorimeter and how it works read your textbook. Look out for the difference in the conditions of pressure between the bomb calorimeter and the enthalpy of combustion apparatus you used in Experiment 4.

EXERCISE 48
Answers on page 101

Figure 14 represents a bomb calorimeter.

Figure 14
A bomb calorimeter.

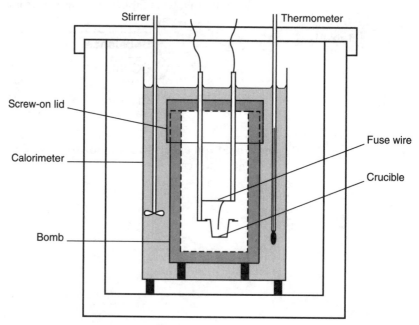

a What substance would be put into:
  i)   the crucible,
  ii) the bomb,
  iii) the calorimeter?
b How is the combustion initiated?
c Why is the energy produced by the complete combustion of one mole of the substance in this apparatus **not** the same as the enthalpy change of combustion of the substance? (Hint: see page 7 for conditions of pressure for measuring ΔH.)

Under the conditions of constant volume employed in the bomb, the energy change measured is known as the internal energy change (symbol: ΔU), and not enthalpy change, ΔH. However, the value of ΔU can be converted to ΔH using the expression:

$$\Delta H = \Delta U + \Delta n\, RT$$

where T = average water temperature in the calorimeter,
  R = gas constant,
  Δn = increase in number of moles of gases during the reaction,

This expression is derived in Appendix 2.

2 INTERNAL ENERGY CHANGE, ΔU

The symbol U represents a property called the internal energy which, like H, has a definite value for a given system in a given state.

OBJECTIVES

When you have finished this appendix you should be able to:
■ explain the term **internal energy change**;
■ derive the equation relating ΔH to ΔU and use it in calculations.

Consider the same reaction

$$Mg\ (s) + 2HCl\ (aq) \rightarrow MgCl_2\ (aq) + H_2\ (g)$$

taking place in each set of apparatus shown in Fig. 15. In **a** the tap is open; in **b** it is closed.

Figure 15

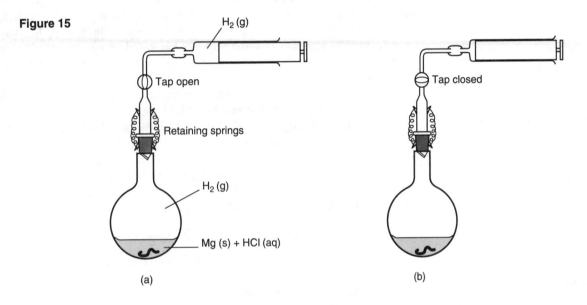

(a)   (b)

Let us suppose that equal amounts of reactants are used in each case, and that it is possible to measure the heat given out to the surroundings in cooling to the original temperature. Do you think the quantities of heat given out in (a) and (b) will be the same? Give this a few moments thought before going on.

In fact, a little more heat will be given out in (b) where the evolved gas is unable to expand into the syringe. The reason is this: in (a) the evolved gas will push the piston of the syringe outwards **against the pressure of the atmosphere**, i.e. it will do work against the atmosphere; this will use up some of the energy which would otherwise be given out as heat. In (b) the reaction takes place at constant volume, and no work is done against the atmosphere; thus, more energy is available for evolution as heat than in (a).

In (a) the heat change at constant pressure is called an **enthalpy change** (symbol: ΔH), an energy change with which you should now be familiar.

In (b) the heat change at constant volume is called an **internal energy change** (symbol: ΔU). This is the energy change which is measured in a bomb calorimeter. (See Appendix 1.)

The reaction in Fig. 15 is one in which gas is evolved. For a reaction in which gas is used up, the system contracts at constant pressure and, in this case, the atmosphere does work on the system so that the enthalpy change ΔH is numerically greater than the internal energy change ΔU.

■ A2.1 Relationship between ΔU and ΔH

The first law of thermodynamics (the law of conservation of energy) states that in any conversion of energy from one form to another, or to heat or to work, no energy is either created or destroyed. (There are many alternative ways of expressing this, as you will find when reading different textbooks.)

An important consequence of this law is that for a system undergoing a change in its internal energy, the total work and/or heat changes involved must equal the change in internal energy.

This can be expressed as

$$\Delta U = \Delta H - w \tag{1}$$

where w is the work done by the system against the atmosphere. (w is negative if the atmosphere does work on the system, as in a reaction where gas is used up.)

Note that the difference between ΔH and ΔU is significant only for reactions involving changes in the amounts of gases present. The small volume changes encountered in most other reactions mean that, in elementary work, the difference between ΔH and ΔU may be ignored.

We now show you how we can convert expression (1) into a form which will enable us to calculate ΔU values from given ΔH values and vice versa.

For a reaction taking place at constant (atmospheric) pressure, the work done against the atmosphere, w, is given by

$$w = \text{force} \times \text{distance}$$

Dividing and multiplying by area,

$$w = \frac{\text{force}}{\text{area}} \times \text{distance} \times \text{area}$$
$$= \text{pressure} \times \text{volume change} = p\Delta V$$

So, the relationship (1) becomes

$$\Delta U = \Delta H - p\Delta V \tag{2}$$

Now the pressure, volume and temperature of an amount of gas are related by the ideal gas equation,

$$pV = nRT \tag{3}$$

where R is the universal gas constant. (You will study this equation further in ILPAC Volume 9, The Gaseous State.) For a reaction at constant pressure and temperature where the increase in volume is ΔV and the increase in the amount of gas is Δn, equation (3) becomes

$$p\Delta V = \Delta nRT$$

Substituting this expression into equation (2) gives

$$\Delta U = \Delta H - \Delta nRT$$

For the reaction at constant pressure and 298 K:

$$Mg \text{ (s)} + 2HCl \text{ (aq)} \rightarrow MgCl_2 \text{ (aq)} + H_2 \text{ (g)}; \Delta H^\circ = -463 \text{ kJ mol}^{-1}$$

$$\Delta n = +1 \text{ mol}, T = 298 \text{ K}, R = 8.31 \text{ J K}^{-1} \text{ mol}^{-1} \text{ and } \Delta H = -463 \text{ kJ}$$

$$\therefore \quad \Delta U = \Delta H - \Delta nRT = -463 \text{ kJ} - (1 \text{ mol} \times \frac{8.31}{1000} \text{ kJ K}^{-1} \text{ mol}^{-1} \times 298 \text{ K})$$

$$= (-463 - 2.47) \text{ kJ} = -465 \text{ kJ and } \Delta U^\circ = \mathbf{-465 \text{ kJ mol}^{-1}}$$

Note that even in a reaction involving the production of gas, the difference between ΔU° and ΔH° is seldom great.

Now try some similar calculations for yourself.

EXERCISE 49

Answers on page 101

Calculate ΔU° for the reactions:
a $BaCO_3 \text{ (s)} \rightarrow BaO \text{ (s)} + CO_2 \text{ (g)}; \quad \Delta H^\circ = +267 \text{ kJ mol}^{-1}$
b $N_2 \text{ (g)} + 3H_2 \text{ (g)} \rightarrow 2NH_3 \text{ (g)}; \quad \Delta H^\circ = -92 \text{ kJ mol}^{-1}$
c $C_6H_6 \text{ (l)} + 3H_2 \text{ (g)} \rightarrow C_6H_{12} \text{ (l)}; \quad \Delta H^\circ = -208 \text{ kJ mol}^{-1}$

ANOTHER PRACTICAL APPLICATION OF HESS' LAW

This determination of an enthalpy change which cannot be measured directly is an alternative to Experiment 3. You use better apparatus, but you need to work more carefully and the calculation is a little more difficult.

EXPERIMENT 6 Using Hess' law

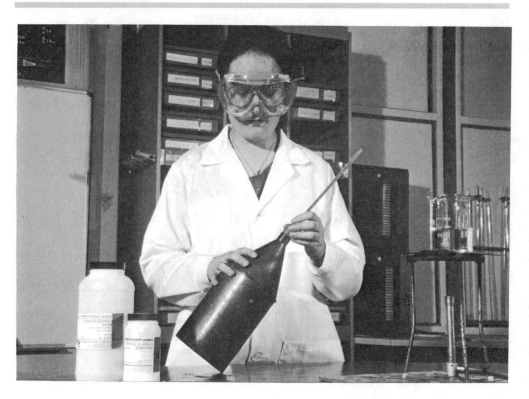

Aim The purpose of this experiment is to determine the enthalpy change for the reaction

$$CuSO_4 \text{ (s)} + 5H_2O \text{ (l)} \rightarrow CuSO_4 \cdot 5H_2O \text{ (s)}$$

Introduction Because $CuSO_4$ (s) is slow to dissolve, and $\Delta H^\ominus$ is small, it is best to do this experiment in a vacuum flask. However, the flask has a measurable heat capacity which you must determine before you proceed with the experiment.

To calculate the required enthalpy change, you perform two 'heat of solution' determinations. You should calculate the masses of the salts and water required. Base your calculations on the following equations

$$CuSO_4 \text{ (s)} + 100H_2O \text{ (l)} \rightarrow CuSO_4 \text{ (aq, 100H_2O)}$$

$$CuSO_4 \cdot 5H_2O \text{ (s)} + 95H_2O \text{ (l)} \rightarrow CuSO_4 \text{ (aq, 100H_2O)}$$

and use 0.025 mol of the appropriate salt in each of the determinations. Show your calculations to your teacher just in case you have made an error which would spoil your laboratory work.

Requirements
- safety spectacles
- vacuum flask with thermometer fitted
- pipette, 50 cm^3
- distilled water
- 2 beakers, 100 cm^3
- Bunsen burner, tripod, gauze and bench mat

- thermometer, 0–100°C
- access to balance (weighing to nearest 0.01 g)
- 2 weighing bottles
- spatula
- anhydrous copper(II) sulphate, $CuSO_4$
- copper(II) sulphate-5-water, $CuSO_4 \cdot 5H_2O$, finely ground beforehand (harmful if swallowed or if dust is inhaled)

Figure 16

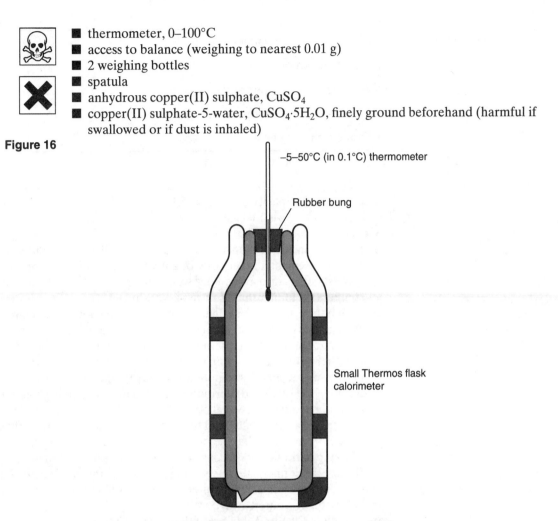

–5–50°C (in 0.1°C) thermometer

Rubber bung

Small Thermos flask calorimeter

Procedure

A. **Determination of the heat capacity of the vacuum flask**

1. Check that the inside of the vacuum flask is reasonably dry and pipette into it 50 cm³ of distilled water at room temperature.
2. Place the thermometer-fitted bung in position and shake gently. Make sure that the entire inside surface of the flask is wet. To read the steady temperature, hold the bung firmly in and turn the flask on its side so that the water covers the mercury reservoir of the thermometer. Read the steady temperature to the nearest 0.1°C. Leave the bung and thermometer in position.
3. Pipette 50 cm³ of distilled water into a clean, dry 100 cm³ beaker and heat it gently until its temperature reaches about 40°C – use a small 0–100°C thermometer. Remove from heat.
4. Use the thermometer from the vacuum flask (with bung still fitted) to gently stir the water in the beaker to ensure its temperature is uniform throughout. Record this temperature to the nearest 0.1°C.
5. **Immediately** pour all of the warmed distilled water into the vacuum flask, close with bung and thermometer, shake gently and note the steady temperature to the nearest 0.1°C. Remember to wet the inside surface and tilt the flask to read the temperature as before.
6. Complete Results Table 7 and then, if you have time, repeat the procedure. It is good practice to do the determination twice and average the results. Furthermore, because this is the first time you have done such an experiment, the second determination should improve your technique.
7. To make best use of laboratory time, we suggest that you complete parts B and C of the experiment before calculating the heat capacity of the flask.

Results Table 7	Mass of cold water in vacuum flask	g	g
	Mass of warm water added	g	g
	Initial temperature of flask and cold water	°C	°C
	Initial temperature of warm water	°C	°C
	Final temperature of flask and mixture	°C	°C

(Specimen results on page 101.)

The specific heat capacity of water is $4.18 \text{ kJ kg}^{-1} \text{K}^{-1}$.
The density of water is 1.00 g cm^{-3}.

B. **Heat of solution of $CuSO_4$ (s)**
1. Rinse the inside of the vacuum flask with distilled water **and drain well**.
2. Weigh the calculated quantity of anhydrous copper(II) sulphate ($CuSO_4$), to the nearest 0.01 g, into a clean dry weighing bottle. (**Do not keep bottle lids and/or stoppers off longer than is necessary**. Why not?)
3. Weigh the appropriate calculated quantity of water, to the nearest 0.1 g, into a dry 100 cm³ beaker, and then pour this water into the vacuum flask. (If the balance you are using has sufficient overall weighing capacity, you may weigh the water directly into the vacuum flask – why is it better to do this?) Close with bung and thermometer, shake, and note the steady temperature, tilting the flask as before.
4. Remove the bung and thermometer from the vacuum flask and quickly and carefully tip **all** of the weighed sample of anhydrous copper(II) sulphate into the water. Replace the bung and thermometer, shake to dissolve the salt, and note the temperature once it has become steady. **This last step may take up to 15 min** (shaking periodically) because the anhydrous salt is often very slow to dissolve.
5. Return the copper sulphate solution to the technician. It could be used for other experiments. If it is not required it must be diluted with a large volume of water before being poured away.
6. Complete Results Table 8 and then move on to part C.

Results Table 8	Mass of anhydrous copper(II) sulphate	g
	Mass of water	g
	Initial temperature of vacuum flask and water	°C
	Maximum temperature of vacuum flask and solution	°C

(Specimen results on page 102.)

C. **Heat of solution of $CuSO_4 \cdot 5H_2O$ (s)**
Wash out your apparatus and then repeat the procedure in part B using the hydrated salt ($CuSO_4 \cdot 5H_2O$). In this second determination the salt dissolves quickly in step 4 and the final steady temperature will be obtained within half a minute. Complete Results Table 9.

Results Table 9	Mass of anhydrous copper(II) sulphate-5-water	g
	Mass of water	g
	Initial temperature of vacuum flask and water	°C
	Maximum temperature of vacuum flask and solution	°C

(Specimen results on page 102.)

Calculation

Answers on page 102

A (heat capacity of flask)

1. Since the flask is insulated, no heat energy is transferred between system and surroundings (in this case, the flask is part of the system). Therefore you can write:

$$\left[\begin{array}{c}\text{Change in heat}\\\text{energy of flask}\end{array}\right] + \left[\begin{array}{c}\text{Change in heat}\\\text{energy of cold water}\end{array}\right] + \left[\begin{array}{c}\text{Change in heat}\\\text{energy of warm water}\end{array}\right] = 0$$

2. In each case, the change in heat energy = heat capacity $\times \Delta T$
   and for the water, heat capacity = mass $\times$ specific heat capacity
   $$= \text{mass} \times 4.18 \text{ kJ kg}^{-1} \text{ K}^{-1}$$

3. Substitute values from Results Table 7 into these expressions and so obtain a value for the heat capacity, C, of the flask. Remember that ΔT is positive for the flask and the cold water but negative for the hot water, and also that the mass must be in kg.

B and C (enthalpy changes)

1. Again, there is no heat energy transfer between system and surroundings so that:

$$\left[\begin{array}{c}\text{Change in heat}\\\text{energy of flask}\end{array}\right] + \left[\begin{array}{c}\text{Change in heat}\\\text{energy of contents}\end{array}\right] + \left[\begin{array}{c}\text{Enthalpy change}\\\text{of solution}\end{array}\right] = 0$$

2. Use this expression and values from Results Tables 8 and 9 to obtain the enthalpy changes for dissolving the weighed amounts of the two salts. Ignore the very small heat capacities of the salts, i.e. use the mass and specific heat capacity of the **water** in your calculations.

3. Scale up to the amounts shown in the equations.

4. Use Hess' law to calculate the required standard enthalpy change.

Questions

Answers on page 103

1. Suggest a reason why it would be difficult to determine, by **direct** experiment, $\Delta H^{\ominus}$ for the reaction

$$CuSO_4 \text{ (s)} + 5H_2O \text{ (l)} \rightarrow CuSO_4 \cdot 5H_2O \text{ (s)}$$

2. Why is it good practice to replace the stoppers/lids of chemical bottles as soon as possible?

3. Why, in step 3 of part B of the experiment, would it be better to weigh the water directly into the vacuum flask rather than in a beaker?

ANSWERS

(Answers to questions from examination papers are provided by ILPAC and not by the examination boards.)

EXERCISE 1   Standard conditions are: $T = 298$ K (25°C), $p = 1.00$ atm, $c = 1.00$ mol dm^{-3}.

EXERCISE 2   **a** i)   exothermic,
                       ii) endothermic,
                       iii) exothermic,
                       iv) exothermic,
                       v)   endothermic.

   b An **increase** in any quantity X gives a **positive** value for ΔX. In an endothermic reaction heat energy must be transferred from the surroundings to the system to maintain constant temperature, i.e. the standard enthalpy ($\Delta H^{\ominus}$) of the system **increases** and $\Delta H^{\ominus}$ is **positive**. Similarly, in an exothermic reaction, the enthalpy of the system **decreases** and $\Delta H^{\ominus}$ is negative.

EXERCISE 3   The energy-level diagram shows that

$$2H_2O \text{ (g)} \rightarrow 2H_2O \text{ (l)}; \Delta H^{\ominus} = -(572 - 484) \text{ kJ mol}^{-1} = -88 \text{ kJ mol}^{-1}$$

   or, for one mole, $\mathbf{H_2O \text{ (g)} \rightarrow H_2O \text{ (l)}; \Delta H^{\ominus} = -44 \text{ kJ mol}^{-1}}$

EXERCISE 4   **a** C (graphite) + O_2 (g) $\rightarrow CO_2$ (g); $\Delta H^{\ominus} = -394$ kJ mol^{-1}
                       C (diamond) + O_2 (g) $\rightarrow CO_2$ (g); $\Delta H^{\ominus} = -396$ kJ mol^{-1}

   b

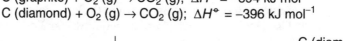
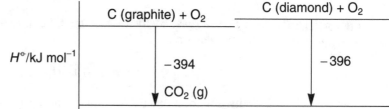

   c The energy-level diagram shows that

   $H^{\ominus}$(diamond) = $H^{\ominus}$(graphite) + 2 kJ mol^{-1}

   For the reaction C (graphite) $\rightarrow$ C (diamond),

   $\Delta H^{\ominus} = H^{\ominus}$(diamond) $- H^{\ominus}$(graphite) = **+2 kJ mol^{-1}**

EXERCISE 5   **a**

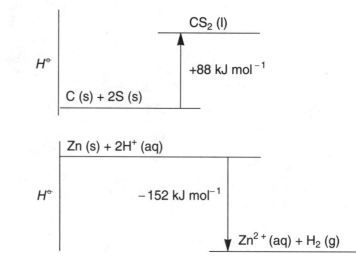

EXERCISE 6   Only those substances which actually take part in the reaction affect the value of $\Delta H^\ominus$. Because enthalpies are additive, for the first diagram we can write:

$$\Delta H^\ominus = H^\ominus(\text{products}) - H^\ominus(\text{reactants})$$
$$= H^\ominus(CO_2) - H^\ominus(C) - H^\ominus(O_2) = -394 \text{ kJ mol}^{-1}$$

Similarly, for the second diagram, we can write:

$$\Delta H^\ominus = H^\ominus(CO_2) + 2H^\ominus(O_2) - H^\ominus(C) - 3H^\ominus(O_2)$$
$$= H^\ominus(CO_2) - H^\ominus(C) - H^\ominus(O_2) = -394 \text{ kJ mol}^{-1}$$

EXERCISE 7   **a** i) Enthalpy change of combustion (of ethanol).
   ii) Enthalpy change of solution (of anhydrous copper sulphate).
   iii) Enthalpy change of combustion (of magnesium) or
       enthalpy change of formation (of magnesium oxide).
   iv) Enthalpy change of combustion (of hydrogen) or
       enthalpy change of formation (of water).
   v) Enthalpy change of combustion (of sulphur) or
       enthalpy change of formation (of sulphur dioxide).

b i) $\Delta H_c^\ominus [C_2H_5OH \text{ (l)}] = -1366.7 \text{ kJ mol}^{-1}$.
   ii) $\Delta H_{soln}^\ominus [CuSO_4 \text{ (s)}] = -67.4 \text{ kJ mol}^{-1}$ (see note below).
   iii) $\Delta H_c^\ominus [Mg \text{ (s)}] = \Delta H_f^\ominus [MgO \text{ (s)}] = -601.7 \text{ kJ mol}^{-1}$.
   iv) $\Delta H_c^\ominus [H_2 \text{ (g)}] = \Delta H_f^\ominus [H_2O \text{ (l)}] = -285.9 \text{ kJ mol}^{-1}$.
   v) $\Delta H_c^\ominus [S \text{ (s)}] = \Delta H_f^\ominus [SO_2 \text{ (g)}] = -296.9 \text{ kJ mol}^{-1}$.

Some data books give slightly different values. This may apply throughout ILPAC. Note that some data books list ΔH_{soln} only at infinite dilution ($-73.3 \text{ kJ mol}^{-1}$ for $CuSO_4$), and others list only the heat of formation of the solution from water and the **elements** of the solute ($-837.3 \text{ kJ mol}^{-1}$ for $CuSO_4$). In the latter case, ΔH_{soln} is obtained by subtracting $\Delta H_f^\ominus$ for the solute, i.e. $\Delta H_{soln}^\ominus [CuSO_4 \text{ (s)}] = \Delta H_f^\ominus [CuSO_4 \text{ (aq)}] - \Delta H_f^\ominus [CuSO_4 \text{ (s)}]$.

EXERCISE 8   **a** $CH_4 \text{ (g)} + 2O_2 \text{ (g)} \rightarrow CO_2 \text{ (g)} + 2H_2O \text{ (l)}$; $\Delta H^\ominus = -890.4 \text{ kJ mol}^{-1}$
b $Ca \text{ (s)} + \frac{1}{2}O_2 \text{ (g)} \rightarrow CaO \text{ (s)}$; $\Delta H^\ominus = -635.5 \text{ kJ mol}^{-1}$
c $Br_2 \text{ (l)} \rightarrow Br_2 \text{ (l)}$; $\Delta H^\ominus = 0.0 \text{ kJ mol}^{-1}$ (i.e. there is no reaction)
d Again $\Delta H^\ominus = 0.0 \text{ kJ mol}^{-1}$ because there is no reaction. Remember that the heat of formation of any element in its standard state is zero for the same reason.

EXERCISE 9   **a** $2Ca \text{ (s)} + O_2 \text{ (g)} \rightarrow 2CaO \text{ (s)}$; $\Delta H^\ominus = -1271.0 \text{ kJ mol}^{-1}$
b $\frac{1}{2}N_2 \text{ (g)} + \frac{3}{2}H_2 \text{ (g)} \rightarrow NH_3 \text{ (g)}$; $\Delta H^\ominus = -46.0 \text{ kJ mol}^{-1}$
c $MgCl_2 \text{ (s)} + 500H_2O \text{ (l)} \rightarrow MgCl_2 \text{ (aq, 500H}_2\text{O)}$; $\Delta H = -152.9 \text{ kJ mol}^{-1}$ (see Ex. 7)
d $C_2H_6 \text{ (g)} + \frac{7}{2}OO_2 \text{ (g)} \rightarrow 2CO_2 \text{ (g)} + 3H_2O \text{ (l)}$; $\Delta H^\ominus = -1559.8 \text{ kJ mol}^{-1}$

EXERCISE 10   **a** $C \text{ (s)} + O_2 \text{ (g)} \rightarrow CO_2 \text{ (g)}$; $\Delta H^\ominus = -394 \text{ kJ mol}^{-1}$
b i) Part **a** shows the enthalpy change for 1.00 mol of carbon. For 10.0 mol the enthalpy change is

$$10.0 \text{ mol} \times (-394 \text{ kJ mol}^{-1}) = \textbf{-3940 kJ}$$

   ii) For 0.25 mol of carbon

$$\Delta H = 0.25 \text{ mol} \times (-394 \text{ kJ mol}^{-1}) = \textbf{-98.5 kJ}$$

   iii) Amount of carbon $= \dfrac{m}{M} = \dfrac{18.0 \text{ g}}{12.0 \text{ g mol}^{-1}} = 1.5 \text{ mol}$

$$\therefore \Delta H = 1.5 \text{ mol} \times (-394 \text{ kJ mol}^{-1}) = \textbf{-591 kJ}$$

c i) You may be able to see at a glance that 197 is half 394, so that the amount of carbon is $\frac{1}{2}$ mol and the mass is 6 g. Otherwise, since the quantity of heat depends directly on the amount of carbon burned:

$$\frac{1.00 \text{ mol of C}}{-394 \text{ kJ}} = \frac{x \text{ mol of C}}{-197 \text{ kJ}}$$

$$\therefore x = \frac{197}{394} = 0.500$$

$\therefore$ mass of carbon $= 0.500$ mol $\times 12.0$ g mol^{-1} = **6.00 g**

ii)

$$\frac{1.00 \text{ mol of C}}{-394 \text{ kJ}} = \frac{y \text{ mol of C}}{-1000 \text{ kJ}}$$

$$\therefore y = \frac{1000}{394} = 2.54$$

$\therefore$ mass of carbon $= 2.54$ mol $\times 12.0$ g mol^{-1} = **30.5 g**

EXPERIMENT 1
*Specimen results and
calculation*

Results Table 1

Time/min	0.0	0.5	1.0	1.5	2.0	2.5	3.0	3.5	4.0	4.5
Temperature/°C	27.0	27.0	27.2	27.2	27.2	27.2	–	66.0	71.4	71.8
Time/min	5.0	5.5	6.0	6.5	7.0	7.5	8.0	8.5	9.0	9.5
Temperature/°C	70.2	68.0	66.2	64.4	62.8	61.0	59.5	58.0	56.6	55.1

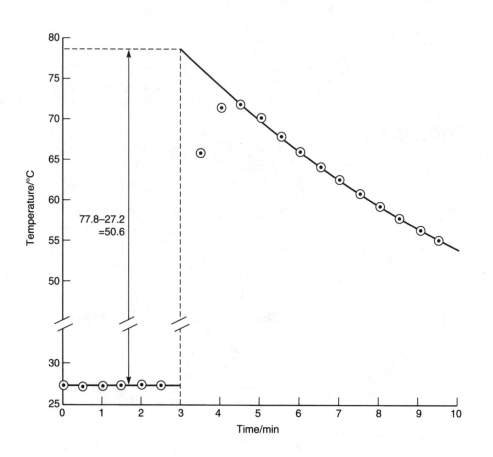

$$\begin{bmatrix}\text{enthalpy change due to} \\ \text{reaction (at constant } T)\end{bmatrix} = \begin{bmatrix}\text{enthalpy change in restoring} \\ \text{solution to original temperature}\end{bmatrix}$$

i.e. ΔH = $mc_p\Delta T$

∴ $\Delta H = mc_p\Delta T = -0.0250$ kg $\times 4.18$ kJ kg^{-1} K$^{-1} \times (-50.6$ K$) = -5.29$ kJ
Amount of Cu^{2+} used $= cV = 1.00$ mol dm$^{-3} \times 0.0250$ dm$^{3}= 0.0250$ mol
Scaling up to the amount in the equation, 1 mol,

$$\Delta H = -5.29 \text{ kJ} \times \frac{1}{0.0250} = \textbf{-212 kJ}$$

Questions

Zn (s) $+ Cu^{2+}$ (aq) $\rightarrow Cu$ (s) $+ Zn^{2+}$ (aq); $\Delta H^{\ominus} = -212$ kJ mol^{-1}

1.

$$\text{Error} = \frac{(-212 - -217) \text{ kJ mol}^{-1}}{-217 \text{ kJ mol}^{-1}} \times 100 = \frac{+5}{-217} \times 100 = \textbf{-2.3\%}$$

2. **a** There is some heat loss from the polystyrene cup.
   b The heat capacity of the solution is not precisely 4.18 kJ kg^{-1} K^{-1}.
   c The density of the solution is not precisely 1.00 g dm^{-3}
   d The heat capacities of the metals were ignored.
   e The thermometer has a small but measurable heat capacity.
3. The reaction takes a few minutes to complete because the copper first precipitated shields some of each zinc particle from the Cu^{2+}.

EXERCISE 11

a

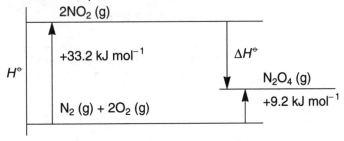

$+33.2$ kJ mol$^{-1} = +9.2$ kJ mol$^{-1} + (-\Delta H^{\ominus})$
∴ $\Delta H^{\ominus} = (9.2 - 33.2)$ kJ mol$^{-1} = \textbf{-24.0 kJ mol}^{-1}$

b

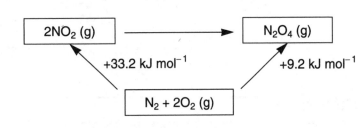

$+33.2$ kJ mol$^{-1} + \Delta H^{\ominus} = +9.2$ kJ mol^{-1}
∴ $\Delta H^{\ominus} = (9.2 - 33.2)$ kJ mol$^{-1} = \textbf{-24.0 kJ mol}^{-1}$

EXERCISE 12

a NH_3 (g) $+ HCl$ (g) $+ \cancel{NH_4Cl\text{ (s)}} + 200H_2O$ (l)
    $\rightarrow \cancel{NH_4Cl\text{ (s)}} + NH_4Cl$ (aq, $200H_2O$); $\Delta H^{\ominus} = (-175.3 + 16.3)$ kJ mol^{-1}
   NH_3 (g) $+ HCl$ (g) $+ 200H_2O$ (l) $\rightarrow NH_4Cl$ (aq, $200H_2O$); $\Delta H^{\ominus} = \textbf{-159.0 kJ mol}^{-1}$
b NH_3 (g) $+ 100H_2O$ (l) $+ HCl$ (g) $+ 100H_2O$ (l) $+ NH_3$ $\cancel{\text{(aq, }100H_2O)} + HCl$ $\cancel{\text{(aq, }100H_2O)}$
    $\rightarrow NH_3$ $\cancel{\text{(aq, }100H_2O)} + HCl$ $\cancel{\text{(aq, }100H_2O)} + NH_4Cl$ (aq, $200H_2O$);
    $\Delta H^{\ominus} = (-35.6 - 73.2 - 50.2)$ kJ mol^{-1}
   NH_3 (g) $+ HCl$ (g) $+ 200H_2O$ (l) $\rightarrow NH_4Cl$ (aq, $200H_2O$); $\Delta H^{\ominus} = \textbf{-159.0 kJ mol}^{-1}$
c The enthalpy change for the overall process is the same by either Method 1 or Method 2.

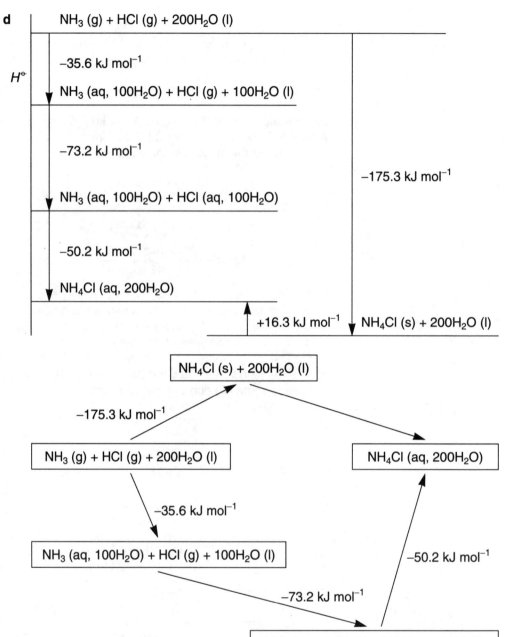

EXPERIMENT 3

Specimen results and calculations

Results Table 2

	MgSO₄	MgSO₄·7H₂O
Mass of weighing bottle	12.91 g	13.42 g
Mass of weighing bottle + salt	15.92 g	19.58 g
Mass of salt	3.01 g	6.16 g
Mass of polystyrene cup	2.10 g	2.36 g
Mass of polystyrene cup + water	47.10 g	44.21 g
Mass of water	45.00 g	41.85 g
Initial temperature	24.1°C	24.8°C
Final temperature	35.4°C	23.4°C

1. $\Delta H = -mc_p\Delta T = -(0.0450 \text{ kg} \times 4.18 \text{ kJ kg}^{-1} \text{ K}^{-1} \times 11.3 \text{ K}) = -2.13 \text{ kJ}$

Scaling up, $\Delta H = -2.13 \text{ kJ} \times \dfrac{1 \text{ mol}}{0.0250 \text{ mol}} = -85.0 \text{ kJ}$

Thus $MgSO_4 \text{ (s)} + 100H_2O \text{ (l)} \rightarrow MgSO_4 \text{ (aq, 100H}_2\text{O)}$; $\Delta H^\ominus = \mathbf{-85.0 \text{ kJ mol}^{-1}}$

2. $\Delta H = -mc_p\Delta T = -(0.04185 \text{ kg} \times 4.18 \text{ kJ kg}^{-1} \text{ K}^{-1} \times (-1.4 \text{ K})) = +0.24 \text{ kJ}$

Scaling up, $\Delta H = +0.24 \text{ kJ} \times \dfrac{1 \text{ mol}}{0.0250 \text{ mol}} = +9.8 \text{ kJ}$

Thus $MgSO_4 \cdot 7H_2O \text{ (s)} + 93H_2O \text{ (l)} \rightarrow MgSO_4 \text{ (aq, 100H}_2\text{O)}$; $\Delta H^\ominus = \mathbf{+9.8 \text{ kJ mol}^{-1}}$

3.

$$\Delta H^\ominus = \Delta H_1 - \Delta H_2 = (-85.0 - 9.8) \text{ kJ mol}^{-1} = \mathbf{-94.8 \text{ kJ mol}^{-1}}$$

Questions 1.

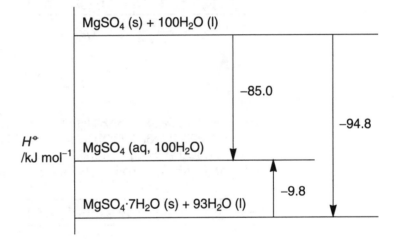

2. The maximum temperature change is much smaller and occurs more quickly.

3. Error $= \dfrac{-94.8 - (-104.0)}{104.0} \times 100 = \mathbf{-8.8\%}$

In addition to the usual assumptions about zero heat transfer between system and surroundings, and the heat capacities of the solutions, impurities in the salts may also affect the results. The anhydrous salt may not be totally free of water, and the hydrated salt may have absorbed extra water.

EXERCISE 13

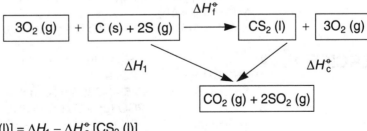

$\Delta H_f^\ominus [CS_2 \text{ (l)}] = \Delta H_1 - \Delta H_c^\ominus [CS_2 \text{ (l)}]$
$\Delta H_1 = \Delta H_f^\ominus [CO_2 \text{ (g)}] + 2\Delta H_f^\ominus [SO_2 \text{ (g)}]$

$\therefore \Delta H_f^\ominus [CS_2 \text{ (l)}] = \Delta H_f^\ominus [CO_2 \text{ (g)}] + 2\Delta H_f^\ominus [SO_2 \text{ (g)}] - \Delta H_c^\ominus [CS_2 \text{ (l)}]$
$\qquad = (-393.5 + 2(-296.9) + 1075.2) \text{ kJ mol}^{-1}$
$\Delta H_f^\ominus [CS_2 \text{ (l)}] = \textbf{+87.9 kJ mol}^{-1}$

EXERCISE 14   a

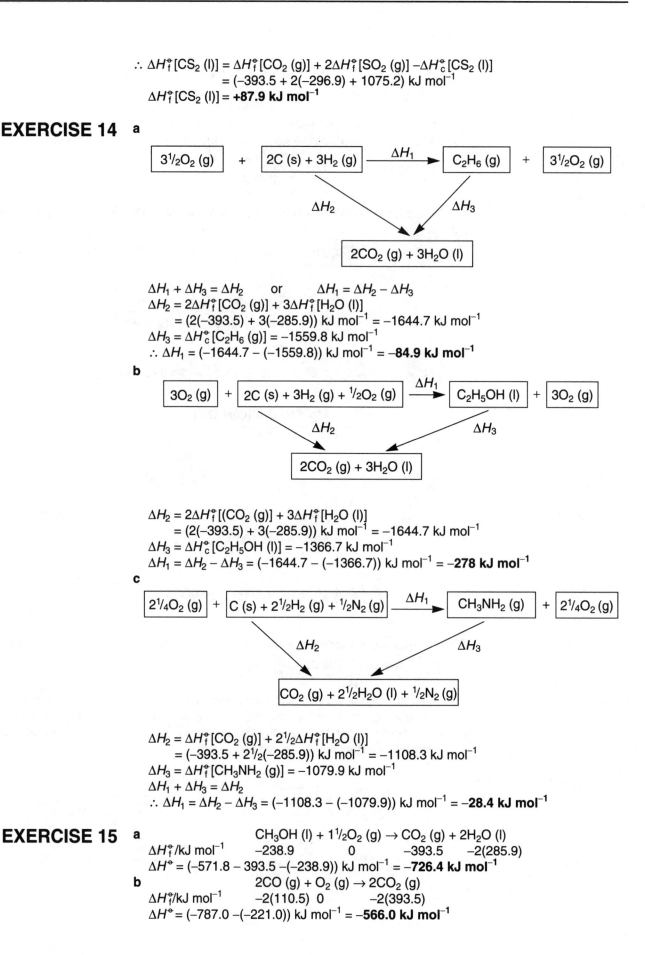

$\Delta H_1 + \Delta H_3 = \Delta H_2 \qquad \text{or} \qquad \Delta H_1 = \Delta H_2 - \Delta H_3$
$\Delta H_2 = 2\Delta H_f^\ominus [CO_2 \text{ (g)}] + 3\Delta H_f^\ominus [H_2O \text{ (l)}]$
$\qquad = (2(-393.5) + 3(-285.9)) \text{ kJ mol}^{-1} = -1644.7 \text{ kJ mol}^{-1}$
$\Delta H_3 = \Delta H_c^\ominus [C_2H_6 \text{ (g)}] = -1559.8 \text{ kJ mol}^{-1}$
$\therefore \Delta H_1 = (-1644.7 - (-1559.8)) \text{ kJ mol}^{-1} = \textbf{-84.9 kJ mol}^{-1}$

b

$\Delta H_2 = 2\Delta H_f^\ominus [(CO_2 \text{ (g)}] + 3\Delta H_f^\ominus [H_2O \text{ (l)}]$
$\qquad = (2(-393.5) + 3(-285.9)) \text{ kJ mol}^{-1} = -1644.7 \text{ kJ mol}^{-1}$
$\Delta H_3 = \Delta H_c^\ominus [C_2H_5OH \text{ (l)}] = -1366.7 \text{ kJ mol}^{-1}$
$\Delta H_1 = \Delta H_2 - \Delta H_3 = (-1644.7 - (-1366.7)) \text{ kJ mol}^{-1} = \textbf{-278 kJ mol}^{-1}$

c

$\Delta H_2 = \Delta H_f^\ominus [CO_2 \text{ (g)}] + 2\tfrac{1}{2}\Delta H_f^\ominus [H_2O \text{ (l)}]$
$\qquad = (-393.5 + 2\tfrac{1}{2}(-285.9)) \text{ kJ mol}^{-1} = -1108.3 \text{ kJ mol}^{-1}$
$\Delta H_3 = \Delta H_f^\ominus [CH_3NH_2 \text{ (g)}] = -1079.9 \text{ kJ mol}^{-1}$
$\Delta H_1 + \Delta H_3 = \Delta H_2$
$\therefore \Delta H_1 = \Delta H_2 - \Delta H_3 = (-1108.3 - (-1079.9)) \text{ kJ mol}^{-1} = \textbf{-28.4 kJ mol}^{-1}$

EXERCISE 15   a

$\qquad\qquad\qquad CH_3OH \text{ (l)} + 1\tfrac{1}{2}O_2 \text{ (g)} \rightarrow CO_2 \text{ (g)} + 2H_2O \text{ (l)}$
$\Delta H_f^\ominus / \text{kJ mol}^{-1} \qquad -238.9 \qquad\quad 0 \qquad\qquad -393.5 \qquad -2(285.9)$
$\Delta H^\ominus = (-571.8 - 393.5 - (-238.9)) \text{ kJ mol}^{-1} = \textbf{-726.4 kJ mol}^{-1}$

b

$\qquad\qquad\qquad 2CO \text{ (g)} + O_2 \text{ (g)} \rightarrow 2CO_2 \text{ (g)}$
$\Delta H_f^\ominus / \text{kJ mol}^{-1} \qquad -2(110.5) \quad 0 \qquad\quad -2(393.5)$
$\Delta H^\ominus = (-787.0 - (-221.0)) \text{ kJ mol}^{-1} = \textbf{-566.0 kJ mol}^{-1}$

c $ZnCO_3 \text{ (s)} \rightarrow ZnO \text{ (s)} + CO_2 \text{ (g)}$
$\Delta H_f^{\ominus}/\text{kJ mol}^{-1}$ −812.5   −348.0   −393.5
$\Delta H^{\ominus} = (-393.5 - 348.0 - (-812.5)) \text{ kJ mol}^{-1} = \textbf{+71.0 kJ mol}^{-1}$

d $2Al \text{ (s)} + Fe_2O_3 \text{ (s)} \rightarrow 2Fe \text{ (s)} + Al_2O_3 \text{ (s)}$
$\Delta H_f^{\ominus}/\text{kJ mol}^{-1}$ 0   −822.2   0   −1675.7
$\Delta H^{\ominus} = (-1675.7 - (-822.2)) \text{ kJ mol}^{-1} = \textbf{−853.5 kJ mol}^{-1}$

[The very large quantity of heat released is sufficient to melt the iron produced and other iron in contact with the reaction mixture. This is the basis of the 'Thermit' process which is still sometimes used to weld steel rails *in situ* on railway tracks.]

EXERCISE 16

$CH_4 \text{ (g)} + H_2O \text{ (g)} \rightarrow CO \text{ (g)} + 3H_2 \text{ (g)}$
$\Delta H_f^{\ominus}/\text{kJ mol}^{-1}$ −75   −242   −110   0
$\Delta H^{\ominus} = (-110 - (-242) - (-75)) \text{ kJ mol}^{-1} = \textbf{+207 kJ mol}^{-1}$

EXERCISE 17

a A compound with a negative value of $\Delta H_f^{\ominus}$ is likely to be stable with respect to decomposition to its elements because that process involves an increase in enthalpy. However, such a substance may be unstable with respect to some other reaction, e.g. combustion, or decomposition to another compound.

b

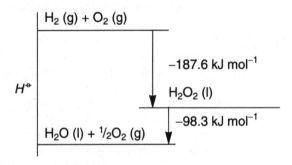

c $H_2O_2 \text{ (l)} \rightarrow H_2O \text{ (l)} + \tfrac{1}{2}O_2 \text{ (g)}$
$\Delta H_f^{\ominus}/\text{kJ mol}^{-1}$ −187.6   −285.9   0
$\Delta H^{\ominus} = -285.9 + 187.6 \text{ kJ mol}^{-1} = \textbf{−98.3 kJ mol}^{-1}$

d $H_2O_2 \text{ (l)}$ is energetically (thermodynamically) stable with respect to its elements; i.e. it will not spontaneously decompose into hydrogen and oxygen. However, $H_2O_2 \text{ (l)}$ is thermodynamically unstable with respect to water and oxygen and may spontaneously decompose to give these products.

EXERCISE 18

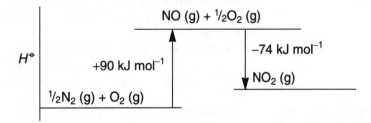

NO (g) in the presence of O_2 is unstable and the two gases react to form NO_2. NO (g) is also unstable relative to the elements and would be expected to decompose spontaneously. However, this reaction is kinetically slower, so the reaction to form NO_2 occurs.

EXERCISE 19

First calculate $\Delta H^{\ominus}$ for the reaction:
$3C_2H_2 \text{ (g)} \rightarrow C_6H_6 \text{ (l)}$
$\Delta H_f^{\ominus}/\text{kJ mol}^{-1}$ +3(226.8)   +49
$\Delta H^{\ominus} = (49.0 - 680.4) \text{ kJ mol}^{-1} = -631.4 \text{ kJ mol}^{-1}$

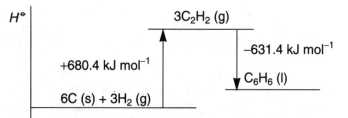

C_2H_2 is energetically unstable with respect to both benzene and its elements. The faster reaction is the one which will occur.

EXERCISE 20   **a** The standard enthalpy of formation is the increase in enthalpy that occurs when one mole of the compound is formed from its constituent atoms, all substances being in their standard states at 298 K (25°C) and 1.00 atm.

b i) $\qquad\qquad CO_2 \text{ (g)} \to CO \text{ (g)} + \frac{1}{2}O_2 \text{ (g)}$

$\Delta H_f^\ominus/\text{kJ mol}^{-1}$ -394 -110 0

$\Delta H^\ominus = -110 + 394 \text{ kJ mol}^{-1} = \textbf{+284 kJ mol}^{-1}$

ii) Both oxides are thermodynamically stable relative to carbon and oxygen because both have negative enthalpies of formation. Decomposition to the elements would involve an increase in enthalpy.

EXERCISE 21   **a** $\qquad\qquad CH_3OH \text{ (l)} + 1\frac{1}{2}O_2 \text{ (g)} \to CO_2 \text{ (g)} + 2H_2O \text{ (l)}$

$\Delta G_f^\ominus/\text{kJ mol}^{-1}$ -166.7 0 -394.4 $-2(237.2)$

$\Delta G^\ominus = (-394.4 - 474.4 - (-166.7)) \text{ kJ mol}^{-1} = \textbf{-702.1 kJ mol}^{-1}$

$(\Delta H^\ominus = -726.4 \text{ kJ mol}^{-1})$

b $\qquad\qquad 2CO \text{ (g)} + O_2 \text{ (g)} \to 2CO_2 \text{ (g)}$

$\Delta G_f^\ominus/\text{kJ mol}^{-1}$ $-2(137.3)$ 0 $-2(394.4)$

$\Delta G^\ominus = (-788.8 - (-274.6)) \text{ kJ mol}^{-1} = \textbf{-514.2 kJ mol}^{-1}$

$(\Delta H^\ominus = -566.0 \text{ kJ mol}^{-1})$

c $\qquad\qquad ZnCO_3 \text{ (s)} \to ZnO \text{ (s)} + CO_2 \text{ (g)}$

$\Delta\Delta G_f^\ominus/\text{kJ mol}^{-1}$ -731.4 -318.2 -394.4

$\Delta G_f^\ominus = (-318.2 - 394.4 - (-731.4)) \text{ kJ mol}^{-1} = \textbf{+18.8 kJ mol}^{-1}$

$(\Delta H^\ominus = +71.0 \text{ kJ mol}^{-1})$

d $\qquad\qquad 2Al \text{ (s)} + Fe_2O_3 \text{ (s)} \to 2Fe \text{ (s)} + Al_2O_3 \text{ (s)}$

$\Delta G_f^\ominus/\text{kJ mol}^{-1}$ 0 -741.0 0 -1582.4

$\Delta G^\ominus = (-1582.4 - (-741.0)) \text{ kJ mol}^{-1} = \textbf{-841.0 kJ mol}^{-1}$

$(\Delta H^\ominus = -853.5 \text{ kJ mol}^{-1})$

In these examples (and many others) the values of $\Delta H^\ominus$ and $\Delta G^\ominus$ are not greatly different and the use of $\Delta H^\ominus$ values to predict the feasibility of reactions would give the correct result.

Note, however, that this only applies to standard conditions, especially $T = 298$ K. ZnO reacts with CO_2 at 298 K, whereas $ZnCO_3$ decomposes readily at higher temperatures. You will see how $\Delta G^\ominus$ varies with temperature later.

EXERCISE 22   **a** Adding the reactions in Table 3 gives the overall reaction:

$$CH_4 \text{ (g)} \to C \text{ (g)} + 4H \text{ (g)}; \Delta H = \textbf{+1662 kJ mol}^{-1}$$

b $\bar{E}(C-H) = (1662 \text{ kJ mol}^{-1}/4) = \textbf{416 kJ mol}^{-1}$

c Each step represents a bond dissociation energy.

d Each bond dissociation energy is different because the environment in each step is different; i.e. the C—H bond broken in

$$\begin{array}{c} H \\ | \\ H - C - H \\ | \\ H \end{array}$$

is different from the ones broken in

$$H - \underset{\cdot\cdot}{\overset{\overset{\displaystyle H}{|}}{C}} - H, \quad H - \underset{\cdot\cdot}{\overset{\displaystyle \cdot}{C}} - H \quad \text{and} \quad \cdot \overset{\displaystyle \cdot}{C} - H$$

EXERCISE 23 **a** Bond energy term is an average value for a given type of bond whereas bond dissociation energy refers to a specific bond in a specific compound.
b Any diatomic molecule; e.g. Cl_2, HBr, CO.

EXERCISE 24

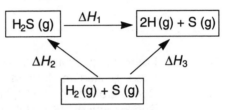

$\Delta H_3 = 2\Delta H_{at}^{\ominus} [H\ (g)] + \Delta H_{at}^{\ominus} [S\ (s)] = (2(218.0) + 238.1)) \text{ kJ mol}^{-1} = 674.1 \text{ kJ mol}^{-1}$
$\Delta H_2 = \Delta H_f^{\ominus}[H_2S\ (g)] = -20.6 \text{ kJ mol}^{-1}$
$\Delta H_1 = -\Delta H_2 + \Delta H_3 = (20.6 + 674.1) \text{ kJ mol}^{-1} = 694.7 \text{ kJ mol}^{-1}$
$\therefore \bar{E}(H{-}S) = 694.7/2 \text{ kJ mol}^{-1} = \textbf{347.4 kJ mol}^{-1}$

EXERCISE 25

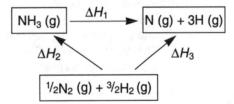

$\Delta H_3 = \Delta H_{at}^{\ominus} [N\ (g)] + 3\Delta H_{at}^{\ominus} [H\ (g)] = (473 + 3(218)) \text{ kJ mol}^{-1} = 1127 \text{ kJ mol}^{-1}$
$\Delta H_2 = -46 \text{ kJ mol}^{-1}$
$\therefore \Delta H_1 = -\Delta H_2 + \Delta H_3 = (46 + 1127) \text{ kJ mol}^{-1} = 1173 \text{ kJ mol}^{-1}$
$\bar{E}(N{-}H) = 1173/3 \text{ kJ mol}^{-1} = \textbf{391 kJ mol}^{-1}$

EXERCISE 26

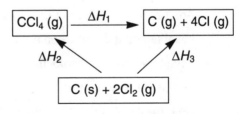

$\Delta H_2 = \Delta H_{at}^{\ominus} [CCl_4\ (l)] + \Delta H_{vap}^{\ominus} [CCl_4\ (l)] = (-135.5 + 30.5) \text{ kJ mol}^{-1} = -105.0 \text{ kJ mol}^{-1}$
$\Delta H_3 = \Delta H_{at}^{\ominus} [C\ (g)] + 4\Delta H_{at}^{\ominus} [Cl\ (g)] = (715.0 + 4(121.1)) \text{ kJ mol}^{-1} = 1199.4 \text{ kJ mol}^{-1}$
$\Delta H_1 = -\Delta H_2 + \Delta H_3 = (105.0 + 1199.4) \text{ kJ mol}^{-1} = 1304.4 \text{ kJ mol}^{-1}$
$\therefore \bar{E}(C{-}Cl) = 1304.4/4 \text{ kJ mol}^{-1} = \textbf{326 kJ mol}^{-1}$

EXERCISE 27

a

Table 4

Alcohol	Bonds broken/mol					Bonds formed	
	C—C	C—H	C—O	O—H	O=O	O=C	O—H
ethanol	1	5	1	1	3	4	6
propan-1-ol	2	7	1	1	4$\frac{1}{2}$	6	8
butan-1-ol	3	9	1	1	6	8	10
pentan-1-ol	4	11	1	1	7$\frac{1}{2}$	10	12
hexan-1-ol	5	13	1	1	9	12	14

b For each pair, combustion of the larger alcohol involves the same number of extra bonds broken and formed as follows:
Bonds broken – 1(C—C), 2(C—H) and 1$\frac{1}{2}$(O=O)
Bonds formed – 2(C=O), 2(O—H)

c See last two lines of table.

d The O=O bonds are identical because they are all in oxygen molecules: the C=O bonds are identical because they are all in CO_2 molecules: the O—H bonds are identical because they are all in H_2O molecules. However, the C—C bonds and the C—H bonds are not identical because they are in different, though similar, molecules. (This applies also to the O—H bonds **broken**.)

e i) The difference in $\Delta H_c^\ominus$ should be almost constant, assuming that the bond energies for C—C, C—H and O—H are almost constant in different alcohols.

ii) The difference in $\Delta H_c^\ominus$ at 298 K should be nearly constant, but slight variations will occur due to the variations in $\Delta H_{vap}^\ominus$.

EXPERIMENT 4

Specimen results and calculation

Results Table 3

	1st run	2nd run	
Molar mass of propan-1-ol, M	60.1	60.1	g mol^{-1}
Initial mass of spirit lamp + alcohol, m_1	13.112	12.083	g
Final mass of spirit lamp + alcohol, m_2	12.083	11.034	g
Mass of alcohol burned, $m_1 - m_2$	1.029	1.049	g
Amount of alcohol burned, $n = (m_1 - m_2)/M$	0.0171	0.0175	mol
Initial temperature of calorimeter	21.7	21.4	°C
Final temperature of calorimeter	33.2	33.0	°C
Temperature change, ΔT	11.5	11.6	K
Heat released during the experiment, ΔH $= \Delta H_c^\ominus$ [propan-1-ol] × amount burned	34.5	35.3	kJ
Heat required for a rise in temperature of 1 K $\dfrac{-2017 \text{ kJ mol}^{-1} \times n}{\Delta T}$ = calibration factor, C	−3.00	−3.04	kJ K^{-1}
Average value of C		−3.02	kJ K^{-1}

Results Table 4

	C_4H_9OH	$C_5H_{11}OH$	$C_6H_{13}OH$	$C_7H_{15}OH$	$C_8H_{17}OH$
Molar mass, M/g mol^{-1}	74.1	88.2	102.2	116.2	130.2
Initial mass of lamp/g	13.691	12.820	13.571	13.679	13.909
Final mass of lamp/g	12.642	12.023	12.668	12.794	13.175
Mass of alcohol burned/g	1.049	0.797	0.903	0.885	0.734
Amount burned, n/mol	0.0142	0.00904	0.00884	0.00762	0.00564
Initial temperature/°C	21.5	21.0	21.7	21.4	22.0
Final temperature/°C	33.5	30.0	33.1	32.2	32.1
Temperature change, ΔT/K	12.0	9.0	11.4	10.8	10.1
$\Delta H_c = \dfrac{C \times \Delta T}{n}$ /kJ mol^{-1}	−2552	−3007	−3895	−4280	−5408

EXERCISE 28

a

Table 5

Alcohol	$\Delta H_c^{\ominus}$/kJ mol^{-1}	Differences/kJ mol^{-1}
propan-1-ol, C_3H_7OH	−2017	
butan-1-ol, C_4H_9OH	−2675	658
pentan-1-ol, $C_5H_{11}OH$	−3323	648
hexan-1-ol, $C_6H_{13}OH$	−3976	653
heptan-1-ol, $C_7H_{15}OH$	−4623	647
octan-1-ol, $C_8H_{17}OH$	−5280	657

b   Average difference in $\Delta H_c^{\ominus}$ for adjacent pairs $= \dfrac{3263}{5} = $ **653 kJ mol^{-1}**

c   It is reasonable to use average bond energy terms for C—C and for C—H in different alcohols, because the heat of combustion data show that the bond dissociation energies do not differ by more than a few kJ mol^{-1}. The difference in heat of combustion between adjacent alcohols in the list is made up from O=O and C=O bond energies which are constant; from $\Delta H_{vap}^{\ominus}$ difference, which is almost constant; and from C—C, C—H and O—H bond energies which must therefore also be nearly constant.

EXERCISE 29

a H_2 (g) + Cl_2 (g) → 2H—Cl (g)
Bonds broken: $\bar{E}$(H—H) + $\bar{E}$(Cl—Cl) = (436 + 242) kJ mol^{-1} = 678 kJ mol^{-1}
Bonds made: $-2\bar{E}$(H—Cl) = −2(431) kJ mol^{-1} = −862 kJ mol^{-1}
∴ $\Delta H^{\ominus}$ = (678 − 862) kJ mol^{-1} = **−184 kJ mol^{-1}**

b N_2 (g) + 3H_2 (g) → 2NH_3 (g)
Bonds broken: $\bar{E}$(N≡N)+ $3\bar{E}$(H—H) = (945 + 3(436)) kJ mol^{-1} = 2253 kJ mol^{-1}
Bonds formed: $-6\bar{E}$(N—H) = −6(389) kJ mol^{-1} = −2334 kJ mol^{-1}
$\Delta H^{\ominus}$ = (2253 − 2334) kJ mol^{-1} = **−81 kJ mol^{-1}**

EXERCISE 30 **a** Bond energy term is the average value of the enthalpy changes for the dissociation of a particular type of bond.

b i) For the reaction

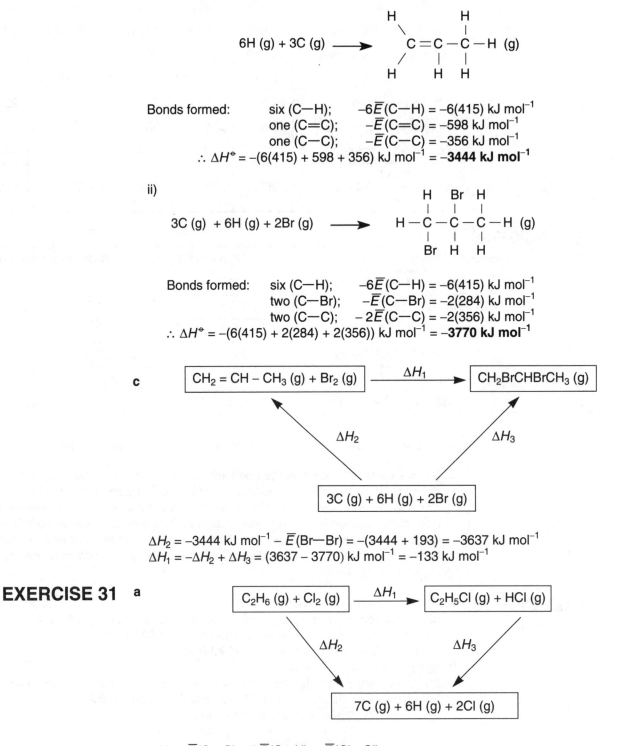

$$6H \text{ (g)} + 3C \text{ (g)} \longrightarrow \begin{array}{c} \text{H} \qquad \text{H} \\ \diagdown \qquad | \\ \text{C}=\text{C}-\text{C}-\text{H (g)} \\ \diagup \qquad | \quad | \\ \text{H} \qquad \text{H} \quad \text{H} \end{array}$$

Bonds formed: six (C—H); $-6\bar{E}$(C—H) $= -6(415)$ kJ mol^{-1}
                    one (C=C); $-\bar{E}$(C=C) $= -598$ kJ mol^{-1}
                    one (C—C); $-\bar{E}$(C—C) $= -356$ kJ mol^{-1}

∴ $\Delta H^{\circ} = -(6(415) + 598 + 356)$ kJ mol^{-1} = **–3444 kJ mol^{-1}**

ii)

$$3C \text{ (g)} + 6H \text{ (g)} + 2Br \text{ (g)} \longrightarrow \begin{array}{c} \text{H} \quad \text{Br} \quad \text{H} \\ | \qquad | \qquad | \\ \text{H}-\text{C}-\text{C}-\text{C}-\text{H (g)} \\ | \qquad | \qquad | \\ \text{Br} \quad \text{H} \quad \text{H} \end{array}$$

Bonds formed: six (C—H); $-6\bar{E}$(C—H) $= -6(415)$ kJ mol^{-1}
                    two (C—Br); $-\bar{E}$(C—Br) $= -2(284)$ kJ mol^{-1}
                    two (C—C); $-2\bar{E}$(C—C) $= -2(356)$ kJ mol^{-1}

∴ $\Delta H^{\circ} = -(6(415) + 2(284) + 2(356))$ kJ mol^{-1} = **–3770 kJ mol^{-1}**

c

$$\boxed{\text{CH}_2 = \text{CH} - \text{CH}_3 \text{ (g)} + \text{Br}_2 \text{ (g)}} \xrightarrow{\Delta H_1} \boxed{\text{CH}_2\text{BrCHBrCH}_3 \text{ (g)}}$$

ΔH_2 ΔH_3

$$\boxed{3C \text{ (g)} + 6H \text{ (g)} + 2Br \text{ (g)}}$$

$\Delta H_2 = -3444$ kJ mol^{-1} $- \bar{E}$(Br—Br) $= -(3444 + 193) = -3637$ kJ mol^{-1}
$\Delta H_1 = -\Delta H_2 + \Delta H_3 = (3637 - 3770)$ kJ mol^{-1} = -133 kJ mol^{-1}

EXERCISE 31 **a**

$$\boxed{\text{C}_2\text{H}_6 \text{ (g)} + \text{Cl}_2 \text{ (g)}} \xrightarrow{\Delta H_1} \boxed{\text{C}_2\text{H}_5\text{Cl (g)} + \text{HCl (g)}}$$

ΔH_2 ΔH_3

$$\boxed{7C \text{ (g)} + 6H \text{ (g)} + 2Cl \text{ (g)}}$$

$\Delta H_2 = \bar{E}$(C—C) $+ 6\bar{E}$(C—H) $+ \bar{E}$(Cl—Cl)
          $= (346 + 6(413) + 242)$ kJ mol^{-1} $= 3066$ kJ mol^{-1}
$\Delta H_3 = \bar{E}$(C—C) $+ 5\bar{E}$(C—H) $+ \bar{E}$(C—Cl) $+ \bar{E}$(H—Cl)
          $= (346 + 5(413) + 339 + 431)$ kJ mol^{-1} $= 3181$ kJ mol^{-1}

$\Delta H_1 = \Delta H_2 - \Delta H_3 = (3066 - 3181)$ kJ mol^{-1} = **−115 kJ mol^{-1}**

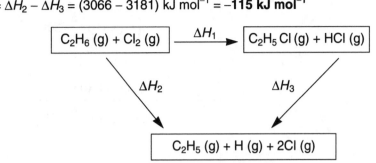

Or, more simply,

$\Delta H_2 = \bar{E}(\text{C—H}) + \bar{E}(\text{Cl—Cl}) = (413 + 242)$ kJ mol^{-1} = 655 kJ mol^{-1}
$\Delta H_3 = \bar{E}(\text{C—Cl}) + \bar{E}(\text{H—Cl}) = (339 + 431)$ kJ mol^{-1} = 770 kJ mol^{-1}
$\Delta H_1 = \Delta H_2 - \Delta H_3 = (655 - 770)$ kJ mol^{-1} = **−115 kJ mol^{-1}**

b　　　　　　　　　　C_2H_6 (g) + Cl_2 (g) → C_2H_5Cl (g) + HCl (g)
$\Delta H_f^\ominus$/kJ mol^{-1}　　　　−84.6　　　0　　　　−136.5　　　−92.3
$\Delta H^\ominus = (-136.5 - 92.3 - (-84.6))$ kJ mol^{-1} = **−144.2 kJ mol^{-1}**

c The bond energy terms $\bar{E}(\text{C—H})$ and $\bar{E}(\text{C—Cl})$ used in the first calculation are average values and are not quite the same as the bond dissociation energies for the particular compounds C_2H_6 and C_2H_5Cl. If the bond dissociation energies were known and used in the calculation they would give a more accurate result, much closer to −144.2 kJ mol^{-1}. Even then, however, the two answers might not quite agree because there is some uncertainty in data book values for $\Delta H_f^\ominus$ and bond

EXERCISE 32　**a**

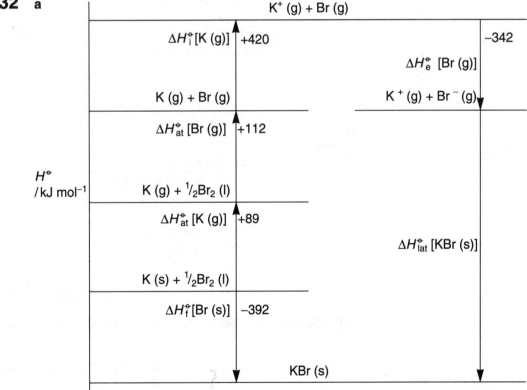

$\Delta H_{\text{lat}}^\ominus$ [KBr (s)] = − [392 + 89 + 112 + 420 − 342] kJ mol^{-1} = **−671 kJ mol^{-1}**

b

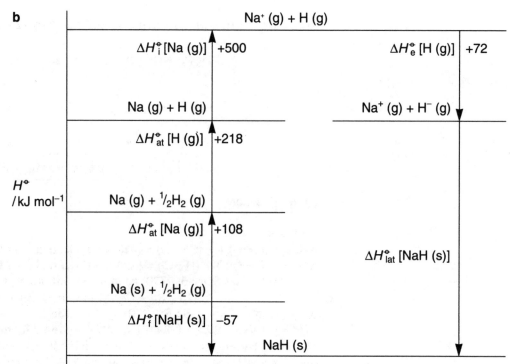

dissociation energies.

EXERCISE 33 a

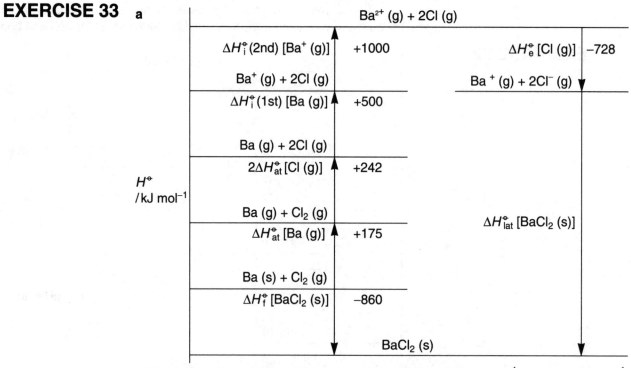

$\Delta H_{lat}^{\ominus}$ [BaCl$_2$ (s)] = $-$ [860 + 175 + 242 + 500 + 1000 $-$ 728] kJ mol^{-1}= **$-$2049 kJ mol^{-1}**

$\Delta H_{lat}^{\ominus}$ [NaH (s)] = $-$[57 + 108 + 218 + 500 $-$ 72] kJ mol^{-1} = **$-$811 kJ mol^{-1}**

b

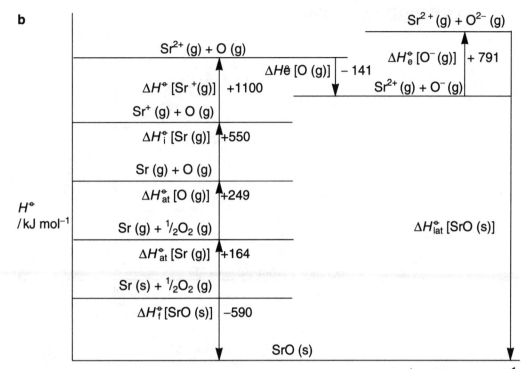

$\Delta H^{\ominus}_{\text{lat}}$ [SrO (s)] = − [590 + 164 + 249 + 550 + 1100 − 141 + 791] kJ mol⁻¹ = **−3303 kJ mol⁻¹**

EXERCISE 34

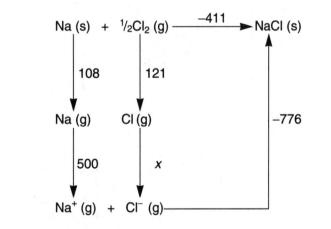

−411 = 108 + 500 + 121 + x − 776
∴ x = −411 − 108 − 500 − 121 + 776 = −364
and $\Delta H^{\ominus}$ = **−364 kJ mol⁻¹**

EXERCISE 35   **a**   i)   B is the sum of the first and second ionisation energies of calcium.
ii)   C is twice the enthalpy change of atomisation of chlorine.
iii)   E is the lattice energy of CaCl₂ (s).
iv)   F is the enthalpy change of formation of CaCl₂ (s).
b   F = A + B + C + D + E
∴ D = F − A − B − C − E = (−795 − 177 − 1690 − 242 + 2197) kJ mol⁻¹
                          = **−707 kJ mol⁻¹**
(This is twice the electron affinity of chlorine.)

EXERCISE 36   a MgCl

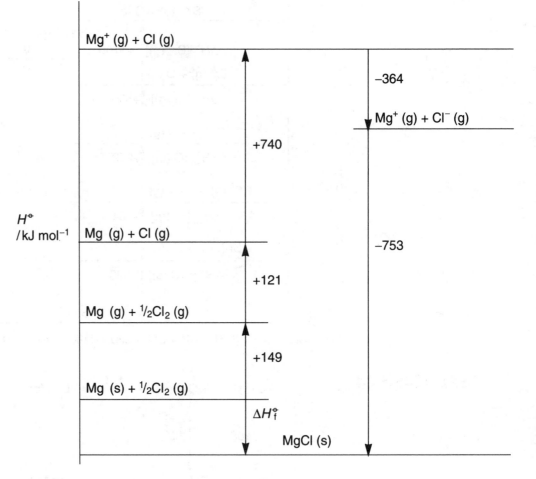

MgCl₂

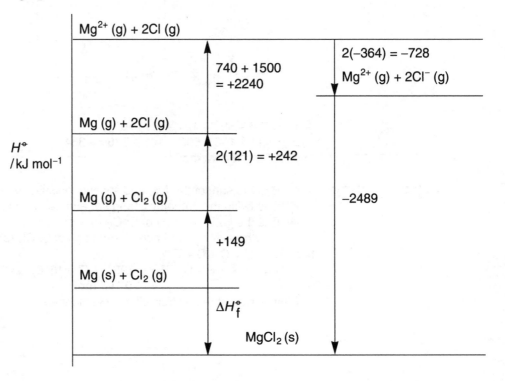

MgCl$_3$

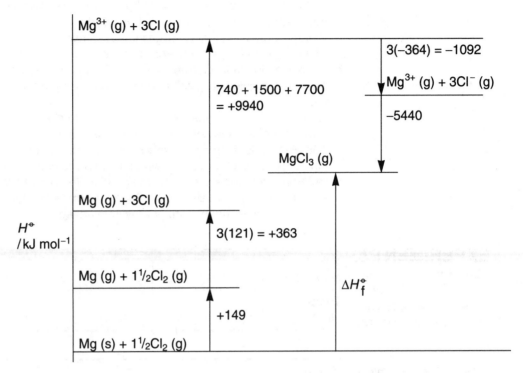

Mg^{3+} (g) + 3Cl (g)

3(−364) = −1092

Mg^{3+} (g) + 3Cl$^-$ (g)

−5440

740 + 1500 + 7700
= +9940

MgCl$_3$ (g)

Mg (g) + 3Cl (g)

$H^{\ominus}$
/kJ mol^{-1}

3(121) = +363

Mg (g) + 1½Cl$_2$ (g)

$\Delta H_f^{\ominus}$

+149

Mg (s) + 1½Cl$_2$ (g)

b $\Delta H_f^{\ominus}$ [MgCl] = (149 + 121 + 740 − 364 − 753) kJ mol^{-1} = **−107 kJ mol^{-1}**.
  $\Delta H_f^{\ominus}$ [MgCl$_2$] = (149 + 242 + 2240 − 728 − 2489) kJ mol^{-1} = **−586 kJ mol^{-1}**.
  $\Delta H_f^{\ominus}$ [MgCl$_3$] = (149 + 363 + 9940 − 1092 − 5440) kJ mol^{-1} = **+3920 kJ mol^{-1}**.

c MgCl and MgCl$_2$ are both energetically stable with respect to the elements, but MgCl$_2$ is more stable than MgCl.

d $\qquad\qquad\qquad$ 2MgCl (s) → MgCl$_2$ (s) + Mg (s)
  $\Delta H_f^{\ominus}$/kJ mol^{-1} $\qquad$ −214 $\qquad\quad$ −586 $\qquad$ 0
  $\Delta H^{\ominus}$ = Σ$\Delta H_f^{\ominus}$[products] − Σ$\Delta H_f^{\ominus}$[reactants]
  $\qquad$ = (−586 + 214) kJ mol^{-1} = **−372 kJ mol^{-1}**

e MgCl is unstable relative to MgCl$_2$ and Mg. This explains why MgCl is unknown; as soon as it forms, it would be converted into MgCl$_2$ and Mg.

EXERCISE 37
a NaCl (s) → Na$^+$ (g) + Cl$^-$ (g); $\Delta H^{\ominus}$ = −$\Delta H_{lat}^{\ominus}$ = +780 kJ mol^{-1}.
b Na$^+$ (g) + aq → Na$^+$ (aq); $\Delta H^{\ominus}$ = $\Delta H_{hyd}^{\ominus}$ (Na$^+$) = −406 kJ mol^{-1}.
  Cl$^-$ (g) + aq → Cl$^-$ (aq); $\Delta H^{\ominus}$ = $\Delta H_{hyd}^{\ominus}$ (Cl$^-$) = −364 kJ mol^{-1}.
c $\qquad$ NaCl (s) → Na$^+$ (g) + Cl$^-$ (g); $\Delta H^{\ominus}$ = +780 kJ mol^{-1}.
  $\qquad$ Na$^+$ (g) + aq → Na$^+$ (aq); $\Delta H^{\ominus}$ = −406 kJ mol^{-1}.
  $\qquad$ Cl$^-$ (g) + aq → Cl$^-$ (aq); $\Delta H^{\ominus}$ = −364 kJ mol^{-1}.
  Overall: NaCl (s) + aq → Na$^+$ (aq) + Cl$^-$ (aq);
  $\qquad$ $\Delta H^{\ominus}$ = (+780 − 406 − 364) kJ mol^{-1} = **+10 kJ mol^{-1}**.
  The overall process is the dissolving of sodium chloride and the enthalpy change is $\Delta H_{solution}$.

EXERCISE 38
a A is the lattice enthalpy of calcium chloride.
  B is the enthalpy of solution of calcium chloride.
  C is the enthalpy of hydration of calcium chloride.
b $B = C − A = \Delta H_{hyd}^{\ominus}$ (Ca^{2+}) + 2$\Delta H_{hyd}^{\ominus}$ (Cl$^-$) − $\Delta H_{lat}^{\ominus}$ (CaCl$_2$)
  $\qquad$ = {−1561 − 2(384) − (−2197)} kJ mol^{-1}
  $\qquad$ = **−132 kJ mol^{-1}**

EXERCISE 39

a K$^+$ and Ba^{2+} have almost the same radius but Ba^{2+} has a very much greater hydration enthalpy. Li$^+$ and Mg^{2+} have radii which differ by only about 10% or 11% but the hydration enthalpy of Mg^{2+} is nearly four times as great as that of Li$^+$. Clearly, increasing ionic charge increases hydration enthalpy very markedly (doubling the charge gives approximately four times the hydration enthalpy).

b Increasing the ionic charge increases the force of attraction between the ion and the polar water molecules and therefore increases the energy released when they come together.

c As ionic radius increases for ions of the same charge, hydration enthalpy decreases (though the effect is not as marked as that for increasing charge).

d The electric field strength is much greater around a small ion than around a large ion of the same charge, so that polar water molecules are more strongly attracted. (Alternatively we can say that water molecules can approach the centre of charge of a small ion more closely and are therefore more strongly bonded.) Stronger attractive forces mean more energy is released.

EXPERIMENT 5
Specimen results and calculation

Results Table 5
Titration of hydrochloric acid

Volume added/cm^3	0.0	5.0	10.0	15.0	20.0	25.0	30.0	35.0	40.0	45.0	50.0
Temperature/°C	22.2	24.4	26.4	28.4	30.1	31.1	30.4	29.9	29.2	28.8	28.2

Results Table 6
Titration of ethanoic acid

Volume added/cm^3	0.0	5.0	10.0	15.0	20.0	25.0	30.0	35.0	40.0	45.0	50.0
Temperature/°C	21.0	22.6	24.3	25.9	27.2	28.7	28.6	28.0	27.5	27.0	26.5

1 and 2.

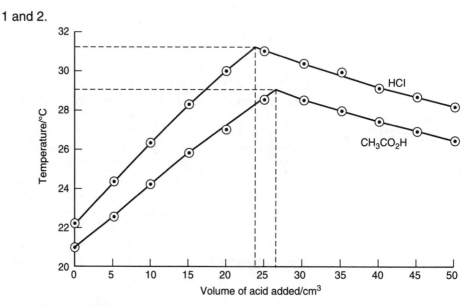

3. **a** HCl (aq) + NaOH (aq) → NaCl (aq) + H$_2$O (l)
Amount of HCl = amount of NaOH

$$c \times \frac{23.5}{1000} \text{ dm}^3 = 1.00 \text{ mol dm}^{-3} \times \frac{50.0}{1000} \text{ dm}^3$$

$$\therefore c = 1.00 \text{ mol dm}^{-3} \times \frac{50.0}{23.5} = \textbf{2.13 mol dm}^{-3}$$

b CH_3CO_2H (aq) + NaOH (aq) → CH_3CO_2Na (aq) + H_2O (l)
Amount of CH_3CO_2H = amount of NaOH

$$c \times \frac{26.5}{1000} \text{ dm}^3 = 1.00 \text{ mol dm}^{-3} \times \frac{50.0}{1000} \text{ dm}^3$$

$$\therefore c = 1.00 \text{ mol dm}^{-3} \times \frac{50.0}{26.5} = \textbf{1.89 mol dm}^{-3}$$

4. **a** Volume of mixture when reaction is complete = (50.0 + 23.5) cm^3 = 73.5 cm^3
ΔT = (31.3 − 22.2) K = 9.1 K
$\Delta H = -mc_p\Delta T$ = −0.0735 kg × 4.18 kJ kg^{-1} K^{-1} × 9.1 K = −2.80 kJ
Amount of NaOH used = cV = 1.00 mol dm^{-3} × 0.0500 dm^3 = 0.0500 mol

Scaling up to 1 mol, ΔH = −2.80 kJ × $\dfrac{1}{0.0500}$ = −56.0 kJ

$\therefore$ HCl (aq) + NaOH (aq) → NaCl (aq) + H_2O (l); ΔH° = **−56.0 kJ mol^{-1}**

b Volume of mixture when reaction is complete = (50.0 + 26.5) cm^3 = 76.5 cm^3
ΔT = (29.1 − 21.0) K = 8.1 K
$\Delta H = -mc_p\Delta T$ = −0.0765 kg × 4.18 kJ kg^{-1} K^{-1} × 8.1 K = −2.59 kJ

Scaling up to 1 mol, ΔH = −2.59 kJ × $\dfrac{1}{0.0500}$ = −51.8 kJ

$\therefore$ CH_3CO_2H (aq) + NaOH (aq) → CH_3CO_2Na (aq) + H_2O (l); ΔH° = **−51.8 kJ mol^{-1}**

Questions 1. The enthalpy change of neutralisation for completely ionised acids and bases is constant because the reaction is the same in every case.

$$H^+ \text{ (aq)} + OH^- \text{ (aq)} \rightarrow H_2O \text{ (l)}$$

2. Some heat is lost from the reaction mixture. The specific heat capacity of the mixture is not precisely 4.18 kJ kg^{-1} K^{-1}.

3. The enthalpy change of neutralisation for incompletely ionised acids and/or bases is less negative because some energy is required to complete the ionisation before the reaction between hydrogen ion and hydroxide ion can occur.

EXERCISE 40 Entropy increases as temperature rises. The molecules acquire more energy, and there are therefore more ways of sharing the total energy between the molecules – this is what is meant by saying that the substance becomes more disordered. If the temperature rise is sufficient to cause a change in state (i.e. melting or vaporisation) there is a considerable increase in disorder and, therefore, in entropy.

EXERCISE 41 **a** $S^\circ[I_2 \text{ (s)}]$ = 117 J K^{-1} mol^{-1}
$S^\circ[Br_2 \text{ (l)}]$ = 152 J K^{-1} mol^{-1}
$S^\circ[Cl_2 \text{ (g)}]$ = 223 J K^{-1} mol^{-1}
$S^\circ[H_2O \text{ (l)}]$ = 70.0 J K^{-1} mol^{-1}
$S^\circ[H_2O \text{ (g)}]$ = 189 J K^{-1} mol^{-1}
N.B. Some data books give values per mole of **atoms** of the halogens.

EXERCISE 42 **a** Decrease. Two moles of gas form one mole thereby decreasing the disorder.
b Decrease. Four moles of gas form two moles thereby decreasing the disorder.
c Increase. Two moles of solid produces two moles of another solid plus one mole of a gas.

EXERCISE 43

a
$$H_2 (g) + C_2H_4 (g) \rightarrow C_2H_6 (g)$$

$S^\ominus$/J K^{-1} mol^{-1} 130.6   219.5   229.5

$\Delta S^\ominus = (229.5 - (130.6 + 219.5))$ J K^{-1} mol^{-1} = **–120.6 J K^{-1} mol^{-1}**

b
$$N_2 (g) + 3H_2 (g) \rightarrow 2NH_3 (g)$$

$S^\ominus$/J K^{-1} mol^{-1} 191.4 3×130.6 2×192.5

$\Delta S^\ominus = (385.0 - (191.4 + 391.8))$ J K^{-1} mol^{-1} = **–198.2 J K^{-1} mol^{-1}**

c
$$2NaNO_3 (s) \rightarrow 2NaNO_2 (s) + O_2 (g)$$

$S^\ominus$/J K^{-1} mol^{-1} 2×116.3 2×120.5 204.9

$\Delta S^\ominus = (204.9 + 241.0 - 232.6)$ J K^{-1} mol^{-1} = **+213.3 J K^{-1} mol^{-1}**

EXERCISE 44

a Negative. $\Delta S^\ominus = (289 - (198 + 223))$ J K^{-1} mol^{-1} = **–132 J K^{-1} mol^{-1}**

b Positive. $\Delta S^\ominus = ((2 \times 70.0) + 204.9 - (2 \times 102))$ J K^{-1} mol^{-1} = **+140.9 J K^{-1} mol^{-1}**

c Negative. $\Delta S^\ominus = ((2 \times 213.6 + 70.0) - 219.5 - (3 \times 204.9))$ J K^{-1} mol^{-1}
$$= \mathbf{-337.0 \text{ J K}^{-1} \text{ mol}^{-1}}$$

d Positive. $\Delta S^\ominus = ((2 \times 82.7) + (3 \times 204.9)) - (2 \times 143.0))$ J K^{-1} mol^{-1} = **+494.1 J K^{-1} mol^{-1}**

e Positive. $\Delta S^\ominus = ((2 \times 197.9) - (2 \times 5.7) - 204.9)$ J K^{-1} mol^{-1} = **+179.5 J K^{-1} mol^{-1}**

EXERCISE 45

a
$$2NO (g) + O_2 (g) \rightarrow N_2O_4 (g)$$

$\Delta H_f^\ominus$/kJ mol^{-1} 2×90.4 0   9.2

$S^\ominus$/J K^{-1} mol^{-1} 2×210.5 204.9   304.2

$\Delta H^\ominus = (9.2 - 180.8 - 0)$ kJ mol^{-1} = –171.6 kJ mol^{-1}

$\Delta S^\ominus = (304.2 - 421 - 204.9)$ J K^{-1} mol^{-1} = –321.7 J K^{-1} mol^{-1} = –0.322 kJ K^{-1} mol^{-1}

$\Delta G^\ominus = \Delta H^\ominus - T\Delta S^\ominus = -171.6$ kJ mol^{-1} $- (298$ K $\times (-0.322$ kJ K^{-1} mol$^{-1}))$ = **–75.6 kJ mol^{-1}**

b
$$NH_3 (g) + HCl (g) \rightarrow NH_4Cl (s)$$

$\Delta H_f^\ominus$/kJ mol^{-1} –46.0   –92.3   –315.5

$S^\ominus$/J K^{-1} mol^{-1} 192.5   186.7   94.6

$\Delta H^\ominus = (-315.5 - (-46.0 - 92.3))$ kJ mol^{-1} = –177.2 kJ mol^{-1}

$\Delta S^\ominus = (94.6 - 186.7 - 192.5)$ J K^{-1} mol^{-1} = –284.6 J K^{-1} mol^{-1} = –0.285 kJ K^{-1} mol^{-1}

$\Delta G^\ominus = \Delta H^\ominus - T\Delta S^\ominus = -177.2$ kJ mol^{-1} $- (298$ K $\times (-0.285$ kJ K^{-1} mol$^{-1}))$
$$= \mathbf{-92.3 \text{ kJmol}^{-1}}$$

c
$$H_2O (l) \rightarrow H_2O (g)$$

$\Delta H_f^\ominus$/kJ mol^{-1} –285.9   –241.8

$S^\ominus$/J K^{-1} mol^{-1} 70.0   188.7

$\Delta H^\ominus = (-241.8 - (-285.9))$ kJ mol^{-1} = +44.1 kJ mol^{-1}

$\Delta S^\ominus = (188.7 - 70.0)$ J K^{-1} mol^{-1} = 118.7 J K^{-1} mol^{-1} = + 0.119 kJ K^{-1} mol^{-1}

$\Delta G^\ominus = \Delta H^\ominus - T\Delta S^\ominus = 44.1$ kJ mol^{-1} $- (298$ K $\times 0.119$ kJ K^{-1} mol$^{-1})$ = **+8.6 kJ mol^{-1}**

EXERCISE 46

a As in Exercise 45, $\Delta H^\ominus = -171.6$ kJ mol^{-1} and $\Delta S^\ominus = -0.322$ kJ K^{-1} mol^{-1}

$\Delta G^\ominus = \Delta H^\ominus - T\Delta S^\ominus = -171.6$ kJ mol^{-1} $- (1000$ K $\times (-0.322$ kJ K^{-1} mol$^{-1}))$

     $= (-171.6 + 322)$ kJ mol^{-1} = **+150 kJ mol^{-1}**

This reaction is feasible at 298 K ($\Delta G^\ominus$ negative) but not at 1000 K ($\Delta G^\ominus$ positive).

b As in Exercise 45, $\Delta H^\ominus = -177.2$ kJ mol^{-1} and $\Delta S^\ominus = -0.285$ kJ K^{-1} mol^{-1}

$\Delta G^\ominus = \Delta H^\ominus - T\Delta S^\ominus = -177.2$ kJ mol^{-1} $- (1000$ K $\times (-0.285$ kJ K^{-1} mol$^{-1}))$

     $= (-177.2 + 285)$ kJ mol^{-1} = **+108 kJ mol^{-1}**

This reaction is feasible at 298 K ($\Delta G^\ominus$ negative) but not at 1000 K.

c As in Exercise 45, $\Delta H^\ominus = +44.1$ kJ mol^{-1} and $\Delta S^\ominus = +0.119$ kJ K^{-1} mol^{-1}

$\Delta G^\ominus = \Delta H^\ominus - T\Delta S^\ominus = +44.1$ kJ mol^{-1} $- (1000$ K $\times 0.119$ kJ K^{-1} mol$^{-1})$

         $= (44.1 - 119)$ kJ mol^{-1} = **–75 kJ mol^{-1}**

At 298 K water vaporises only to a small extent ($\Delta G^\ominus$ small and positive) but at 1000 K vaporisation is complete ($\Delta G^\ominus$ substantially negative).

d
$$CaCO_3 \rightarrow CaO (s) + CO_2 (g)$$

$\Delta H_f^\ominus$/kJ mol^{-1} –1206.9   –635.5   –393.5

$S^\ominus$/J K^{-1} mol^{-1} 92.9   39.7   213.6

$\Delta H^\ominus = (-635.5 - 393.5 + 1206.9)$ kJ mol^{-1} = 177.9 kJ mol^{-1}

$\Delta S^\ominus = (213.6 + 39.7 - 92.9)$ J K^{-1} mol^{-1} = 160.4 J K^{-1} mol^{-1}

$\Delta G^{\ominus} = \Delta H^{\ominus} - T\Delta S^{\ominus} = 177.9 \text{ kJ mol}^{-1} - (1000 \text{ K} \times 0.1604 \text{ kJ K}^{-1} \text{ mol}^{-1})$
$= (177.9 - 160.4) \text{ kJ mol}^{-1} = \textbf{+17.5 kJ mol}^{-1}$
This reaction is not feasible at 298 K ($\Delta G^{\ominus}$ substantially positive) but can proceed to an equilibrium mixture of reactants and products at 1000 K ($\Delta G^{\ominus}$ small and positive).

EXERCISE 47

a An endothermic reaction can take place spontaneously if there is an increase in entropy ($\Delta S^{\ominus}$ positive) **and** if the product $T\Delta S^{\ominus}$ is greater than $\Delta H^{\ominus}$. In these circumstances, $\Delta G^{\ominus}$ ($= \Delta H^{\ominus} - T\Delta S^{\ominus}$) will be negative. This is more likely if i) $\Delta H^{\ominus}$ is small, ii) $\Delta S^{\ominus}$ is large (e.g. much gas formed) and iii) T is large.

b In most reactions $\Delta S^{\ominus}$ is very small so that $T\Delta S^{\ominus}$ at 298 K is much smaller numerically than $\Delta H^{\ominus}$. $\Delta G^{\ominus}$ will then have almost the same value as $\Delta H^{\ominus}$, which therefore indicates the feasibility of the reaction.

$$\Delta G^{\ominus} = \Delta H^{\ominus} - T\Delta S^{\ominus} \simeq \Delta H^{\ominus} \text{ if } T\Delta S^{\ominus} \text{ is small}$$

EXERCISE 48

a i) The substance for which the heat of combustion is being determined
  ii) Oxygen at high pressure.
  iii) Water.

b The combustion is started by passing a current through a wire in contact with the substance in the crucible. The wire heats the sample which then burns in the oxygen.

c The energy produced by burning one mole of substance in constant volume conditions is the change in internal energy, ΔU, rather than the change in enthalpy, ΔH.

EXERCISE 49

a $\Delta n = +1$ mol
$\Delta U = \Delta H - \Delta nRT = +267 \text{ kJ} - (1 \text{ mol} \times 8.31 \times 10^{-3} \text{ kJ K}^{-1} \text{ mol}^{-1} \times 298 \text{ K})$
$= (+267 - 2.47) \text{ kJ} = 265 \text{ kJ}$ $\therefore \Delta U^{\ominus} = \textbf{265 kJ mol}^{-1}$

b $\Delta n = -2$ mol
$\Delta U = \Delta H - \Delta nRT = -92 \text{ kJ} - (-2 \text{ mol} \times 8.31 \times 10^{-3} \text{ kJ K}^{-1} \text{ mol}^{-1} \times 298 \text{ K})$
$= (-92 + 5.0) \text{ kJ} = -87 \text{ kJ}$ $\therefore \Delta U^{\ominus} = \textbf{-87 kJ mol}^{-1}$

c $\Delta n = -3$ mol
$\Delta U = \Delta H - \Delta nRT = -208 \text{ kJ} - (-3 \text{ mol} \times 8.31 \times 10^{-3} \text{ kJ K}^{-1} \text{ mol}^{-1} \times 298 \text{ K})$
$= (-208) + 7.4) \text{ kJ} = -201 \text{ kJ}$ $\therefore \Delta U^{\ominus} = \textbf{-201 kJ mol}^{-1}$

EXPERIMENT 6

Specimen results and calculations

Results Table 7

Mass of cold water in vacuum flask	50.0 g	50.0 g
Mass of warm water added	50.0 g	50.0 g
Initial temperature of flask and cold water	23.1°C	23.5°C
Initial temperature of warm water	41.3°C	45.2°C
Final temperature of flask and mixture	31.0°C	33.0°C

$$\left[\begin{array}{c}\text{Change in heat}\\\text{energy of flask}\end{array}\right] + \left[\begin{array}{c}\text{Change in heat}\\\text{energy of cold water}\end{array}\right] + \left[\begin{array}{c}\text{Change in heat energy}\\\text{of warm water}\end{array}\right] = 0$$

1) $[C \times (31.0 - 23.1) \text{K}] + [0.0500 \text{ kg} \times 4.18 \text{ kJ kg}^{-1} \text{ K}^{-1} \times (31.0 - 23.1) \text{ K}]$
$+ [0.0500 \text{ kg} \times 4.18 \text{ kJ kg}^{-1} \text{ K}^{-1} \times (41.3 - 31.0) \text{ K}] = 0$
$(C \times 7.9 \text{ K}) + (1.65 \text{ kJ}) + (-2.15 \text{ kJ}) = 0$

$$\therefore C = \frac{(2.15 - 1.65) \text{ kJ}}{7.9 \text{ K}} = 0.063 \text{ kJ K}^{-1}$$

2) $(C \times 9.5\ K) + (1.99\ kJ) + (-2.55\ kJ) = 0$

$$\therefore C = \frac{(2.55 - 1.99)\ kJ}{9.5\ K} = 0.059\ kJ\ K^{-1}$$

Mean value of C = **0.061 kJ K^{-1}**

Results Table 8	Mass of anhydrous copper(II) sulphate	3.99 g
	Mass of water	45.0 g
	Initial temperature of vacuum flask and water	22.5°C
	Maximum temperature of vacuum flask and solution	27.5°C

$$\begin{bmatrix} \text{Change in heat} \\ \text{energy of flask} \end{bmatrix} + \begin{bmatrix} \text{Change in heat} \\ \text{energy of contents} \end{bmatrix} + \begin{bmatrix} \text{Enthalpy change} \\ \text{of solution} \end{bmatrix} = 0$$

$(0.061\ kJ\ K^{-1} \times 5.0\ K) + (0.0450\ kg \times 4.18\ kJ\ kg^{-1}\ K^{-1} \times 5.0\ K) + \Delta H = 0$
$0.305\ kJ + 0.941\ kJ + \Delta H = 0 \qquad\qquad \therefore \Delta H = -1.25\ kJ$

Scaling up to 1 mol, $\Delta H = -1.25\ kJ \times \dfrac{1}{0.025} = -50\ kJ$

$\therefore CuSO_4\ (s) + 100H_2O\ (l) \rightarrow CuSO_4\ (aq,\ 100H_2O);\ \Delta H^{\circ} = $ **-50 kJ mol^{-1}**

Results Table 9	Mass of anhydrous copper(II) sulphate-5-water (0.0250 mol)	6.24 g
	Mass of water added (0.025 × 95 mol)	42.75 g
	Initial temperature of vacuum flask and water	23.0°C
	Maximum temperature of vacuum flask and solution	21.8°C

$$\begin{bmatrix} \text{Change in heat} \\ \text{energy of flask} \end{bmatrix} + \begin{bmatrix} \text{Change in heat} \\ \text{energy of contents} \end{bmatrix} + \begin{bmatrix} \text{Enthalpy change} \\ \text{of solution} \end{bmatrix} = 0$$

$0.061\ kJ\ K^{-1} \times (-1.2\ K) + (0.0450\ kg \times 4.18\ kJ\ kg^{-1}\ K^{-1} \times -1.2\ K) + \Delta H = 0$
(Note that the total mass of water in the contents is the same in both experiments.)
$-0.0732\ kJ + (-0.226\ kJ) + \Delta H = 0 \qquad\qquad \therefore \Delta H = +0.299\ kJ$

Scaling up to 1 mol, $\Delta H = +0.299\ kJ \times \dfrac{1}{0.025} = +12.0\ kJ$

$\therefore CuSO_4 \cdot 5H_2O\ (s) + 95H_2O\ (l) \rightarrow CuSO_4\ (aq,\ 100H_2O);\ \Delta H^{\circ} = $ **$+12.0$ kJ mol^{-1}**

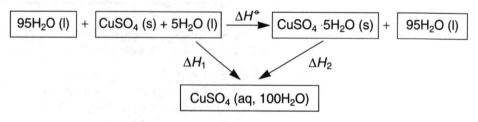

$\Delta H^{\circ} = \Delta H_1 - \Delta H_2 = -50\ kJ\ mol^{-1} - 11.5\ kJ\ mol^{-1} = -62\ kJ\ mol^{-1}$

Questions   1. The reaction would be extremely slow (even with excess water as in the experiment you have done, it was quite slow).

2. Replacing lids and stoppers prevents moisture being absorbed from the air (especially important for anhydrous copper sulphate). Also, stoppers left off can be exchanged by mistake causing contamination of the contents when eventually replaced.

3. It is impossible to transfer **all** the weighed quantity from a beaker to the flask.